THE NEW BASIC READERS

CURRICULUM FOUNDATION SERIES

THE NEW
Streets and Roads

William S. Gray, A. Sterl Artley, May Hill Arbuthnot

SCOTT, FORESMAN AND COMPANY

Chicago · Atlanta · Dallas · New York

Stories

On the Road to Storyland

Animals in Town and Country

On the Roads of Long Ago

3

On
City Streets

The Queer Noise

John and Susan Hall and their little brother Tommy lived in a large city. Their home was on the second floor of a big building.

Tim White lived on the top floor of the same building. One morning Tim knocked on the Hall family's door.

"Hurry!" he called. "Let me in!"

Susan ran to open the door.

"What's the matter, Tim?" she asked.

"Did you hear a queer noise in our building last night?" Tim asked.

"What noise?" asked John Hall. "I didn't hear anything."

"What was it like?" asked Susan.

Tim said, "I thought it sounded like clothes flapping in the wind."

"I can't think of anything that sounds like that," said John.

"Oo-oo! I'm scared," said Tommy.

Tim smiled and said, "I think you're safe down here, Tommy. I heard the noise on the top floor, where I live."

"Well," said John, "maybe we should try to find out what made that noise. Do you think anyone would care if we went up and looked around?"

"I don't think anyone would mind," said Tim. "Let's go!"

The four children ran up the stairs. When they reached the top floor, they listened quietly for a few minutes.

Suddenly they heard something.

"That's it!" Tim whispered. "That's the queer noise I heard."

"It does sound like clothes flapping in the wind," whispered Susan. "What is it?"

"I don't know," answered John.

Tommy did not say a word. He just held onto Susan's hand.

They listened again. The queer noise seemed to be coming from a room that had a sign on its door. The sign said "Storeroom."

Tim held up his hand and said, "Shh." Then he walked over to the storeroom. He stopped in front of the door and tried to open it.

Tommy held his breath. He wondered what would happen next. But nothing happened. The door would not open.

"We need help," said Tim. "Maybe Mr. Waters, the watchman, can help us."

"I'll run and get him," said John. "You and Susan and Tommy stay here."

Soon John came back with Mr. Waters.

"What's going on here?" asked the watchman.

Tim said, "I heard a queer noise last night. Now I know where it's coming from. It's in the storeroom."

Mr. Waters walked to the heavy door and listened. He heard the noise, too.

"Stand back," he said, "until I see if it's safe in here."

The children stood very close together. Tommy was so scared that he closed his eyes and held his breath.

The watchman pushed on the door, but it would not open. Then he pushed harder, and suddenly the door flew wide open.

The flapping noise was even louder now. But the storeroom was dark, and the children were too scared to look inside. They just stood at the door and listened.

Suddenly Tim whispered, "Something is flying around in there! That's what is making the flapping noise."

Just then five birds came flying out!

Mr. Waters ran to open the window in the hall. The children waved their arms until all the birds flew out. Then the watchman quickly shut the window, and everything was quiet.

"I wonder how the birds got in there," Tim said.

"We'll soon find out," said Mr. Waters as he went into the storeroom.

After turning on the light, he called, "Come in, children. Don't be afraid. It's safe in here now."

Slowly the children walked into the room. All but Tommy, who just looked in. He was still so scared that he held his breath.

"See that open window!" Tim shouted. "That's how the birds got in."

"You're right," said Mr. Waters, "and we'll close it this minute. That will put an end to the queer noises in here."

Baby-Sitting with Tommy

Mrs. Hall was going downtown one afternoon. Tommy could not go with her because he had a cold. So Susan and John were staying home with him.

Most of the time Tommy did not mind having his brother and sister take care of him. But today he did mind. He had played indoors all week, and he was tired of it.

John and Susan were trying to think of something to make Tommy happy. But he did not want to do anything.

"Look here, Tommy," said Susan. "We'll start your train."

But Tommy was tired of the train before it had gone even halfway around.

"We could do our magic tricks for you," said John.

But Tommy said, "No."

Then Susan gave him an apple.

But Tommy ate only half of it.

"You could make believe that you're a fireman," said John. "Here's your truck and ladder."

But Tommy just stood and looked at the truck and ladder on the floor.

"I don't know what else we can do," said John.

Then Susan thought of something. She began to whisper to John.

Soon she said, "Oh, Tommy, would you like to play a new game?"

"What game?" asked Tommy.

"A new game called 'Thinking,'" said John. "Susan and I think of something, and you have to guess what it is. Do you want to play?"

"I'd like to try," said Tommy.

John thought for a minute. Then he slowly said, "I am thinking of something tall. You can go up and down this thing. You can carry it all around. Can you guess what it is?"

Tommy thought and thought.

At last he asked, "Is it a stairway? You can go upstairs, and you can go downstairs. It must be a stairway!"

"Now remember, Tommy," said John, "I said that you can carry this thing around. Can you carry a stairway all around?"

Tommy said, "No, but I was half right. I'd better think some more."

Suddenly he picked up a ladder from his toy truck.

"I know!" he shouted. "It's a ladder! It's like this toy ladder. Firemen can carry ladders around. They can go up and down ladders, too!"

"Yes, that's right," cried John. "I was thinking of a ladder all the time."

Tommy felt better now. He thought the game was fun.

"Let's play it again," he said.

This time Susan said, "I am thinking of something that's made of air. You can't see it, but you can make it stop. What is it?"

Tommy thought for a while.

"Is the wind made of air?" he asked. "Is it the wind?"

Susan shook her head. "The wind is made of air," she said, "but you can't make it stop."

Tommy thought a little longer. Then he asked, "Is it something I can buy? Is it a balloon?"

"No," answered Susan. "But that's a good guess. You use what I'm thinking of to make balloons big."

"Oh, I know now!" said Tommy. "It's my breath! I can blow up balloons with my breath. My breath is made of air, and I can stop my breath by holding it."

John laughed and said, "I think you guessed right, Tommy. But Susan fooled me because of one thing she said."

"What did I say?" asked Susan.

"You said we can't see this thing," said John. "But we can when it's cold outside. We can see our breath then!"

"Oh," said Susan, laughing. "I forgot about that. You're too smart, John."

"Now it's your turn to guess," Tommy shouted to Susan and John.

Tommy looked around the room for a minute.

Then he said, "I'm thinking of a thing that you can see through. You can put animals in it. The animals can move around inside it, but they can't get out. I know you can't guess what it is."

"We can see through glass," said John. "If it's made of glass and has fish in it, I know what it is."

"No," said Tommy. "You don't know, because it's not made of glass."

"I give up," said Susan. "You'll have to tell me what it is."

Tommy shouted, "The cage! The bird cage! You can see through the cage, and you can put birds inside it. They can't come out, but they can fly all around inside the cage!"

"You really fooled us," laughed John. "I'd never have thought of a bird cage."

Just then Mrs. Hall came home.

When she asked Tommy how he felt, he said, "Fine! I've been having fun. I've been thinking!"

"Thinking!" said Mother. "Is that fun?"

"Oh, yes," said Tommy. "It's fun to think of things that fool John and Susan."

The Picnic Place

"I'm glad you wanted a picnic, Susan," said John. "I like picnics, too!"

This was Susan Hall's birthday. And on her birthday, her family always did just what Susan wanted.

Everyone was ready to go.

The food was ready, too. John and Tommy were helping Mr. Hall take it out to the car.

Soon everybody got into the car, and the family rode off to the country.

John said, "I think it would be fun to eat our picnic lunch near a farm. Then we could watch all the different animals as we ate."

"I know just the place for Susan's birthday picnic," said Father. "It's near a farm. It's a cool place with tall trees and a pretty little pond."

"Oh, boy!" shouted Tommy. "I'll have a place to sail my boat."

"Where is this place?" asked Susan.

"You'll see it soon," Mr. Hall said. "We turn to the right at the very next stop sign."

But when they came to the place to turn, the road was closed. A sign said "Detour."

"I didn't know that this road had been closed," said Father. "This detour won't take us to the right place. But never mind. We'll take it anyway and find a different place."

They took the detour and rode along for a few minutes.

Suddenly John cried, "What about that place near the grove of trees?"

Mr. Hall stopped the car.

"That looks like a nice, cool place for a picnic," Susan said. "Let's eat there."

Just then three cows came out of the grove and walked toward the car.

"The cows found that cool place first," said Mrs. Hall. "We'll have to find a different place for our picnic."

So they drove on.

After a while Tommy shouted, "Stop! We're passing a nice place. Let's have our picnic here!"

"That does look like a good spot," his father said. "But there are beehives in the field. I don't think you would like a picnic so close to bees."

"Never mind," said Mrs. Hall. "We'll soon find a good place for our picnic."

Everybody sat back in the automobile, and Father drove on.

Soon they came to a river. Nearby was a little grove of maple trees.

"Just the place for our picnic!" said Mr. Hall. "Grass and trees, and some water where Tommy can sail his boat! I'll stop here."

He stopped, and they all got out.

Tommy ran ahead. But when he came to the maple grove, he called Susan.

"There's a sign in big, black letters," he said. "What does it say?"

"It says 'No picnics here,'" Susan told her little brother.

The family got back into the car. On and on they drove without passing any place where they could have a picnic.

Soon they all felt very hot and very hungry.

"I can't wait much longer for lunch," Tommy said.

"Oh, dear!" cried Susan. "Can't we find any place for our picnic?"

"Yes," said Father. "I've just thought of a place. It has trees and grass and a pond with fish in it. Tommy can sail his boat there. It's a fine picnic place."

They drove straight ahead for a while.

"Now, children, shut your eyes," said Mr. Hall. "I'll tell you when we get to the place. Then you may open your eyes. You'll be surprised."

The children closed their eyes and kept them closed. It was hard not to look, but they did not open their eyes once.

At last Father stopped the automobile
and said, "Now you may look!"

The children opened their eyes and got
out of the car.

They saw many big trees.

They saw green grass.

They saw a pond where Tommy could
sail his boat.

But suddenly Tommy saw a sign with
big letters on it.

"Does it say 'No picnics'?" he asked.

"Not this time," said Susan. "This sign
says 'Picnics here.'"

John ran ahead and found a table. Then he helped put the food on it.

All at once John shouted, "See that large building over there! Isn't that where we live? Why, look! We're in the park near our own home!"

"What a joke on us!" laughed Susan. "We rode and rode and rode to find a place for our picnic. And all the time our city park was the very best place!"

The Big, Long Honk

One day Father went to do an errand for Mother. He took the children along.

Susan and John were in the back seat of the car. Tommy sat in the front seat because he liked to see his father drive.

"Please let me honk the horn," Tommy said as they turned a corner. "Please."

"I am sorry, Tommy," said Mr. Hall. "Automobile horns often scare people. You wouldn't want to do that."

"No," said Tommy. "But when I'm big, I'll drive my own car. I'll honk long and loud all the time!"

Just then Tommy's father stopped the automobile in front of a big store.

"I'm going to buy some groceries here," he said. "I'll be right back."

"I'll make believe I'm driving," said Tommy, sliding over on the car seat. "Maybe I'll even honk the horn once."

"Forget about that horn," John said. "Just look at the big truck passing us."

As Tommy turned to look at the passing truck, his arm rested on the wheel.

Honk, honk, honk went the horn.

Quickly Tommy lifted his arm from the wheel, but the horn did not stop.

"Tommy!" cried Susan. "Don't honk the horn. Quit making that terrible noise."

"I'm not honking the horn," laughed Tommy. "Nobody is honking it."

He held up his hands to show that he was not touching the wheel. But the horn kept on making the loud noise.

Then John climbed into the front seat and began to push and pound on the wheel. He pounded and pounded, but he could not stop the honking.

Soon there was a crowd of people on the walk beside the car.

"Just listen to that terrible noise!" said an angry man in the crowd. "And look at that big boy behind the wheel. He's honking that horn. He's big enough to know better."

Tommy began to laugh. "Those people think you are honking the horn," he said to John.

John climbed into the back seat again, and Tommy moved over behind the wheel. "This is a good, long honk," he said.

And it was a long honk. It was the longest and loudest honk that Tommy had ever heard.

People across the street banged their windows shut. Dogs barked, and babies cried. Nobody but Tommy liked the big, long honk.

The street was now filled with cars and a crowd of people.

In a few minutes a policeman came hurrying through the crowd. He looked at Tommy in the front seat.

"Quit making so much noise," he said. "What do you mean by honking that horn?"

"I'm not honking it," cried Tommy. "Nobody is honking it. It started, and now it won't stop. It's stuck."

When Mr. Hall heard the horn, he came hurrying out of the grocery store. Behind him ran the storekeeper, carrying flour and butter and other groceries to the car.

"Tommy!" cried Mr. Hall as he pushed his way through the crowd. "Stop that awful noise! Stop honking that horn! Stop this minute."

"I'm not honking it," Tommy told his father. "Nobody is honking it. It's stuck."

Mr. Hall tried to fix the horn by giving the wheel a little tap. Then he gave it a hard knock. He hammered the wheel with his hand, bumpety-bump-bump!

He pounded and pounded and pounded. But the horn was stuck, and the awful honking kept on.

Mr. Hall turned to the policeman. "I'm sorry," he said. "I can't stop the horn."

Just then a man came running from a filling station on the corner.

"Perhaps I can fix your horn," he said.

The filling-station man looked at the engine. Then he moved something, and the honking stopped.

Suddenly the street seemed very quiet.

"My!" said Mr. Hall. "I'm glad that awful noise has stopped."

"I'm not," laughed Tommy. "I liked it. It was a big, long honk. It was the biggest, longest honk I ever heard."

A Halloween Surprise

Two girls were going downstairs when John Hall met them on his way up.

"John, can you guess who we are?" asked one of the girls.

"Yes, I can guess," laughed John. "You're Nancy Fox and my sister Susan. Why do you have on those fancy clothes?"

"Sam Penny invited us to a Halloween party," Nancy answered. "Sam invited all the boys and girls in our room at school. They will all dress in fancy clothes."

As the girls walked down the street, Susan said, "Look for a big brick house. That's where Sam lives."

Suddenly Nancy cried, "See that boy wearing the fancy clown suit! I'm sure he's Dick. Yesterday Dick told me that he was going to wear a clown suit."

Just then the boy in the clown suit went up the steps of a brick house.

When he knocked on the door, the two girls were right behind him.

A woman wearing a blue dress met them at the door and said, "Come in."

Nancy and Susan laughed at all the funny-looking children dancing about.

There was a funny scarecrow with a big mouth. Next to him was a girl dressed like an ugly old troll. She wore a purple coat and a red-and-purple hat.

A boy with feathers on his head was dancing up and down and shouting. One boy wore a cowboy suit with a fancy handkerchief around his neck.

A boy wearing a fireman's suit was carrying a little toy ladder. One girl was dressed like a fairy, with purple wings.

A big black cat was waving a paper pumpkin and saying, "Mew, mew!"

Then Nancy saw a boy dressed like the big bad wolf. Another boy was the wee, little pig.

The big bad wolf was trying to come through the door. The wee, little pig was holding the door open just a crack.

He called through the crack, "You are the wolf, and you can't come in."

But the wolf pushed the door open. Then he and the pig began to laugh.

The other children laughed, too. Then everyone began to play games.

After a while the woman who had come to the door called to the children.

"Now each one must walk across the room," she said. "If we can guess your name, you must uncover your face."

When the pumpkin girls walked across the room, nobody guessed who they were.

Next came a boy in a dark blue suit with a big silver star on his coat. He was wearing a policeman's cap.

"Oh!" shouted one of the boys. "Look at that fat policeman! He's Sandy."

The fat policeman uncovered his face.

"He's a stranger!" Nancy whispered to Susan.

A white cat with a fiddle got up next. She uncovered her face when her name was guessed. But Nancy and Susan did not know her.

The two girls watched as the other children's names were guessed. But when they uncovered their faces, they were strangers, too.

"This is queer," Susan said to Nancy. "I thought Sam invited just the boys and girls in our room at school. But I don't know anyone here."

"We know the boy wearing the clown suit," said Nancy. "It's Dick. We can't be wrong about that."

But when the clown uncovered his face, Susan said, "He's not Dick! We followed the wrong clown to the wrong party!"

The woman who wore the blue dress smiled at Nancy and Susan. "We haven't guessed the pumpkin girls yet," she said.

Slowly the two girls stood up. But nobody could guess who they were.

Even when the girls uncovered their faces, no one knew them.

Susan was ready to cry.

"We're at the wrong party," she said. "We were invited to Sam Penny's party."

"This is Johnny Ball's party," said the woman. "But we're all glad you came. You surprised us, and it's fun to have a surprise at a Halloween party."

She telephoned Sam and told him where the girls were. Then she brought them sandwiches to eat and milk to drink. After they had ice cream and big pieces of cake, she took them to Sam's house.

And that is how Susan and Nancy went to two Halloween parties in one day.

Lost and Found

One day Mrs. Hall took Susan and two of her friends downtown for lunch.

"What a big place!" said Betty Jane Burns. "Dozens and dozens of tables!"

Betty Jane had come from the farm to visit Susan. Everything in the city was new and different to her.

"I'll have a chicken sandwich with a piece of apple pie," said Mrs. Hall.

Susan and Nancy Fox had the same.

Then Betty Jane said she would have a chicken sandwich and a glass of milk. She had a piece of pie, too.

After eating, they paid the bill. Then they went to a big store.

"Let's ride in the elevator to the fifth floor and look at the dolls," Susan said.

They got in. Then the elevator girl shut the door and started the elevator.

Up, up it went, past floor after floor. When the elevator stopped at the fifth floor, Mrs. Hall and the girls got out.

"Oh, I see the toys," said Betty Jane.

"I'd like to look at the dolls," said Nancy. "But I want to go down that big slide, too. And I want to buy a silver sailboat for my brother."

"All right, Nancy," said Mrs. Hall. "You look for the sailboat while Susan and Betty Jane look at the dolls.

"I'm going to the third floor to buy some shoes and an umbrella. We'll meet here on the fifth floor. Be here at the elevators under the big clock in half an hour."

Each of the three girls took a ride down the red slide. Then Nancy went to buy a toy sailboat.

Betty Jane and Susan looked at toys as they walked along. They passed the bicycles, wagons, and fire engines. Then the two girls came to the dolls.

There were hundreds of dolls.

There was one fairy doll with silver stars all over her dress. Betty Jane stopped and looked at the fairy doll.

"Look, Susan!" she called. "Look at this doll with the silver stars. Isn't it beautiful?"

But Susan was not there.

Betty Jane walked around looking for her. Soon she came to some stairs. What queer stairs they were! They were moving! They were going up, up, up!

People stood on the stairs and rode up to the next floor.

Betty Jane thought, "I'll take a ride on these funny stairs myself."

So she rode the moving stairs up to the next floor.

When she got off, she saw more stairs moving up. So she got on and rode up to the next floor.

Each floor had those moving stairs, and Betty Jane rode up, up, up.

At last she reached the top floor.

"Oh!" Betty Jane thought. "I must go down to the floor where the toys are. Mrs. Hall said we should meet under the clock in half an hour."

Betty Jane got into the elevator and went down to another floor. But there were no boats or bicycles or dolls on that floor. It was full of dozens and dozens of washing machines.

Betty Jane was puzzled and wondered what to do. She went to another floor. There were still no toys or dolls or bicycles. There were just hundreds and hundreds of coats.

Now Betty Jane was more puzzled than ever. She got into the elevator and went down to the next floor.

There were no toys or dolls or bicycles on that floor either. No Nancy! No Susan or Mrs. Hall!

How puzzled Betty Jane was when she looked at the clock above the elevators.

It had been almost an hour since Mrs. Hall had left the three girls.

Betty Jane did not know how to find her friends. So she just walked around.

At last she saw a window with a big sign that said "Lost and Found."

"Oh," thought Betty Jane, "my friends are lost, and I want to have them found. Maybe this woman can find them."

LOST AND FOUND

"Please," Betty Jane said. "My friends are lost. I haven't seen them for an hour. I don't know what became of them. Can you find them for me?"

"Perhaps I can," said the woman. "Is your name Betty Jane Burns?"

"Yes," said Betty Jane, wondering how the woman knew her name.

The woman picked up a telephone and said a few words to someone. Then she put the telephone down and said, "Stay right here."

In a few minutes Mrs. Hall, Nancy, and Susan came running toward Betty Jane.

"Oh, Betty Jane," cried Susan. "We waited half an hour near the fifth-floor elevators. Then we looked everywhere. It was awful to think you were lost."

Betty Jane looked puzzled. "Why, Susan!" she said. "I wasn't lost. You were lost! I'm glad I found you."

Let's Trade

Just before Betty Jane's visit was over, Susan thought of having a party.

"Mother, Mother!" she cried as she ran into the house. "Let's have a trading party for Betty Jane. Let's have the party next Friday."

"I've never heard of a trading party," said Mrs. Hall.

"I haven't either," said John.

"Me either," said Tommy. "What is a trading party?"

"Well, I'll tell you," said Susan. "At a trading party everybody brings a toy or something else to trade.

"Then everybody will trade what he has brought for something that someone else has brought."

"Fine!" said Mrs. Hall. "You may have your party on Friday. But tell your friends what kind of party it is."

Susan asked Tim White and Nancy Fox to come to her trading party on Friday. She told them and all the other children she asked what kind of party it was.

"It's a surprise party for Betty Jane," she said. "So don't tell her anything about it."

On Friday afternoon Mrs. Hall asked Betty Jane to go on an errand.

When she came back from the store, everyone and everything was ready and waiting for her.

When Betty Jane saw all the children, she said, "Oh, oh! Oh, my!"

Everyone laughed at her surprise.

"Here are balloons for everybody," Mrs. Hall said. "This policeman balloon is for Betty Jane. See how he bobs his head at her."

The balloon was tied to a long stick. Every time Betty Jane moved, the fat policeman bobbed his head. He bobbed along right after Betty Jane as she skipped across the room.

All the children had brought things to trade. Mrs. Hall gave Betty Jane a storybook so that she could trade, too.

Tim had brought a funny toy monkey. "This is my monkey, Happy," he said. "I'll trade my monkey for something."

"Would you trade him for this book?" asked Betty Jane. "I'd like your funny toy monkey. I'd like to have Happy."

"I have read that book," said Tim, "but I'll see. Let the others trade first."

Nancy had brought a small bunch of paper flowers to trade.

"I would like to have your bunch of flowers," said Susan. "Maybe you'll trade your pretty purple flowers for my box of silver buttons."

Nancy looked at the silver buttons and then at her bunch of purple flowers.

"My mother is making a new dress for me," Nancy said. "I think those buttons would look pretty on it. I'll trade!"

Next Tommy wanted to trade.

"Does anybody want this pen? Does anybody want to trade for it?" he asked.

Then John said, "Does anybody want to trade something for my roller skates? They're too small for me."

"I do!" said Tommy. "Here is my pen. It's a very good one. Do you want to trade for this pen?"

"All right," said John. "It's a trade!"

Tim and Betty Jane were the only ones left to trade.

"Now, Tim, will you trade with me?" asked Betty Jane.

"I don't know," said Tim. "Is that book the only thing you can trade?"

Betty Jane thought and thought.

"Just a minute," she said. And she ran out of the room.

When Betty Jane came running back, Mrs. Hall was with her.

Betty Jane handed Tim a piece of paper.

"I'll trade this for your toy monkey," Betty Jane said.

Tim read what was on the paper.

I'll trade a whole week's visit at our farm.

Betty Jane

"Does this paper really mean what it says?" asked Tim. "Is it really true?"

"I think so, Tim," said Mrs. Hall. "Betty Jane's family will be very glad to have you visit them."

"Oh, boy!" shouted Tim. "It's a trade! Here, Betty Jane, you may take Happy. When shall I come for my visit?"

"Just any time," said Betty Jane as she took the monkey. "My brother Don and I will be glad to see you any time."

"Oh, boy!" cried Tim again. "A whole week at a farm!"

Tim thought he had traded for the best thing of all.

But Betty Jane, who lived at the farm every day, thought her trade was the best of all.

Along
Country Roads

Who Wants This Dog?

"It's true!" thought Tim White. "My wish to visit a farm is coming true!"

It was near the end of summer, and Tim was going to visit Betty Jane Burns. He was on his way to the farm at last.

For the long trip Tim had to have two tickets. One ticket was for the train. The other ticket was for the bus.

At Spring City Tim got off the train and onto a big bus. He became more and more excited as the bus got closer and closer to Maple Grove Village.

All at once Tim heard the bus driver shout, "Maple Grove!"

Tim jumped up and hurried to the door. As he stepped off the bus, he heard someone call, "Here we are, Tim!"

Then he saw Betty Jane Burns.

Betty Jane said, "I'm glad to see you, Tim. This is my brother Don. Father is over there in the car.

"Come along now, Tim. We have lots of things to do and see on the farm."

"I don't want to miss a thing," said Tim. "Let's hurry!"

As soon as they reached the farm,
Tim wanted to see everything at once.

He saw a field of hay and a big field of
yellow wheat. When he saw the long
rows of tall green corn, he cried, "What
a lot of corn! How many rows do you
raise?"

Don laughed and said, "I'm not sure
how many rows of corn we raise. But
I am sure there are too many to count."

On the way back to the farmhouse,
Tim heard a dog barking.

"Here comes Hurry," Don said.

"He looks like a wonderful dog," said Tim as he rubbed Hurry's head.

The dog wagged his tail. Then Tim rubbed Hurry's head some more.

"I never could have a big dog in the city," Tim said. "But Hurry is just the kind of dog I've always wanted."

Hurry wagged his tail harder.

"I wish you were mine," Tim said as the friendly dog looked up at him.

"Hurry is lots of fun," said Don. "But we may have to give him away."

"Give him away!" cried Tim. "Why?"

"Well," said Don, "my mother raises chickens, and Hurry keeps scaring them. He runs around the chicken yard and barks. He barks at the hens all day long.

"Mother and Father say we'll have to make Hurry stop scaring the hens. If we don't, we'll have to give him away."

"I suppose we could tie him up in the barn," said Betty Jane. "But that wouldn't be fun for any of us."

"We'll have to think of something else," said Don. "I don't even want to think of having to tie Hurry up."

"I'd never want to either," Tim said. "I'd want to play with him all day long if he were mine. Maybe the three of us can think of some way to keep him from scaring the hens."

All day long the children were thinking about the dog. How could they make Hurry stay away from the chicken yard?

In the afternoon the three children took the dog for a walk to the village. On the way Tim was very quiet.

Suddenly he asked, "Do you suppose a scarecrow would keep Hurry away?"

"I don't think so," said Betty Jane. "Hurry is too smart to be scared that way. I don't suppose he can be scared by anything."

At the village store Tim stopped to look at some balloons in the window.

"Oh!" he said. "I've just thought of a plan to scare Hurry! I'm going to buy some of those balloons."

Tim bought five colored balloons.

"Now let's run back to the farm," he said. "If this plan of mine works, the chickens won't be scared any more."

When the children reached the farm, they put Hurry in the house. Don hurried to get some string for Tim. Then he followed his sister and Tim to the chicken yard.

Tim began to blow up a red balloon. When it was very big, he tied it with a piece of string. Then he tied the string to the chicken-yard fence.

"Now bring Hurry out," Tim said.

Don let Hurry out of the house, and the dog came running out to the chicken yard. Then he stopped.

A strange red thing was bobbing on the fence!

Hurry barked at the red thing, but it did not go away. He sniffed at it, but the round, bobbing thing stayed right there.

Hurry sniffed and barked at it again, and suddenly he jumped at it.

BANG!

All at once the big red thing was gone, and so was Hurry! The awful noise had scared him.

Soon he was far, far away from the chicken yard.

"It worked!" shouted Don. "If we tie the other balloons to the fence, I think they'll scare Hurry again. They'll scare him enough to keep him away from the chickens."

"Now we can keep Hurry here at the farm," cried Betty Jane. "We won't have to give him away. I'm glad you thought of your balloon trick, Tim."

"I'm glad, too," said Tim. "I hope this plan of mine keeps on working."

"Oh, I think it will," said Betty Jane. "Hurry doesn't like to have anything go BANG! in his face."

"Who does?" laughed Don.

Bread and Jam

Soon after Tim's visit, Betty Jane and Don had to start to school.

On the first day they started walking down the road to the schoolhouse.

Children from the other nearby farms walked to school, too. Some children rode on the school bus. Others rode in cars and on bicycles. But Sarah Best rode Dusty, her pony.

When Betty Jane saw Sarah, she waved to her. Sarah waved back and tried to make her pony hurry.

Soon a whole crowd of children was at Maple Grove School.

All at once the boys and girls heard the bell. Then they hurried into the schoolroom. Soon they were all sitting at their desks. School had started.

Some of the children began to read. Some began to write stories about their summer fun. Sarah's brother Tom began to draw pictures. One drawing showed Tom on a horse.

All of a sudden there was a buzzing sound. Buzz, zzz, zzz!

"Wasps! Wasps!" screamed Betty Jane. "They'll sting us!"

She waved her book at two wasps that were flying around her desk.

Tom jumped up and knocked the wasps down with his piece of drawing paper. Then he took them to the window and dropped them outside.

"There are a lot more wasps outside!" Tom shouted.

Sarah jumped up from her desk and hurried to the window.

"Look at all the wasps out there!" she said. "And there goes Dusty galloping toward the woods! He's afraid of wasps. He's afraid they'll sting him."

"I'll catch Dusty," said Don Burns, jumping up from his desk. He ran out the side door, but he hurried back in.

"The air is full of wasps!" he cried.

Miss Valentine shut all the windows so that no more wasps could get inside.

"Now!" said the teacher. "We'll have to think of a way to get rid of all those wasps, or we can't go outdoors."

After a minute Don said, "I've thought of a way to get rid of them. We have hives of honeybees at home, and I know that bees like sweet things. Maybe wasps like sweet things, too. Do you suppose they do?"

"Yes," answered Miss Valentine, "I'm sure they like sweet things."

"Betty Jane and I have something very sweet in our lunch boxes," said Don. "We have jam sandwiches. I could take some of the sandwiches outside and walk away from the schoolhouse. Then maybe the wasps would follow the jam."

"Maybe they would," said the teacher. "Let's try it and see."

"Oh, dear!" cried Sarah Best. "I'd hate to have the wasps sting Don."

"We won't let them sting him," said Miss Valentine. "We'll cover him up."

She walked to the back of the room to get her raincoat and an old straw hat.

Don laughed as he buttoned the long coat and pulled the purple hat down on his head.

"Won't the wasps sting Don's face and hands?" asked Sarah.

"We'll cover them, too," answered the teacher. "Then Don will be safe."

When Don was ready, Sarah laughed and said, "What a funny sight he is!"

"The wasps can't scare me now," said Don. "Bring me the jam sandwiches."

Betty Jane opened her lunch box and took out a jam sandwich. She put a piece on each of Don's hands.

"I'd like a bite for myself," she said. "I hate to feed this jam to the wasps."

"Never mind," said Don. "We'll have enough sandwiches for lunch."

He walked to the door holding his hands carefully so that the pieces of bread would not fall off.

Don was so much shorter than Miss Valentine that her coat flapped around his legs. He had to lift each foot carefully as he walked.

"I know I'm a funny sight," laughed Don. "I'd hate to dress like this all the time!"

Tom Best opened the door, and Don stepped out of the schoolhouse.

The children left their desks and ran to the windows to watch Don.

Sure enough, the wasps were following the sweet jam. A few had lighted on it. But Don did not seem to be afraid.

Slowly and carefully he walked with the long coat flapping around his feet at every step he took.

On went Don until he was out of sight in the woods. By this time the jam he carried was covered with wasps.

Soon Don came out of the woods, riding on Dusty.

"All the wasps are gone!" he shouted happily to the children. "I got rid of them. I left them in the woods with the bread and jam."

"What if they fly back?" Betty Jane asked. "What will we do?"

"We'll just feed them more bread and jam," laughed Don.

Big Joe and Little Joe

One morning children were crowding around a big billboard across from Maple Grove School.

"Look at all those animals!" said Tom. "Doesn't that big lion look fierce? And look at that funny giraffe!"

"I think the clowns are funnier," said Betty Jane Burns. "I like them better than the giraffes."

All at once a new voice spoke. "My uncle is with that circus. He's the star clown."

Everyone turned around to see who had spoken. A new boy and girl were standing behind the crowd of children.

"I'm Bill Long," said the boy. "This is my sister Judy. We have just moved to a farm near here."

"Is your uncle really a circus clown?" asked Tom.

"Yes," said Bill, "his name is Big Joe. He has been with that circus for a long time. He always gives us circus tickets. I have my ticket with me."

Bill pulled a ticket out of his pocket and showed it to everyone.

After school Bill and Judy rode home on the bus with the other boys and girls. They all wanted to know more about Big Joe.

Bill and Judy were glad to talk about their uncle. By the time they got off the bus, the children could hardly wait for the circus to come.

At last the big day came.

The Long family had breakfast early that morning. While they were eating, Father got up to answer the telephone.

When he came back, he said, "Bill, I just spoke to your Uncle Joe. He wants us to come down to the circus grounds right now. He wants you to bring the clown suit he gave you."

"I'll be ready in two minutes," said Bill. "But why does Uncle Joe want my clown suit?"

Mr. Long just smiled.

Soon Bill and his father were on their way to the circus grounds. All along the road they saw circus pictures of fierce lions, tall giraffes, and funny clowns.

At last they saw the circus tents just ahead. Mr. Long parked the car near the big gate, and they went inside.

What a busy place it was!

There were men running here and there.

There were trucks moving from place to place loaded with all kinds of things.

Mr. Long looked about and said, "I wonder where we can find Uncle Joe."

"Maybe the man on that load of straw can tell us," said Bill. Then he called out, "We're trying to find Big Joe. Do you know which tent he's in?"

"Certainly," answered the man. "He's in the fifth tent from here."

"Thank you," Bill said as he and his father started down the row of tents.

In the fifth tent they found Big Joe.

"Here we are, Uncle!" Bill cried.

"Hello," shouted Uncle Joe. "I'm glad you came. Did you bring the clown suit?"

"Sure," said Bill. "Do you need it in one of your acts?"

"Well," said Uncle Joe, "I might use it in my last act. I wonder if you would like to be a clown."

"Me!" cried Bill. "A clown?"

"Certainly," said Uncle Joe. "I'll tell you just what to do."

Bill's father smiled and said, "I have to leave now. I'll see you at the circus this afternoon."

First Uncle Joe told Bill just what he wanted him to do in the act. Then they went to another big tent to eat lunch.

Many of the people who worked in the circus were eating there. They sat at long tables that were loaded with food. But Bill was so busy looking around that he almost forgot to eat.

At last it was time for Big Joe and Bill to get ready for their act.

Uncle Joe drew black lines on Bill's chin. He drew a blue line across each eye. He put a big painted nose over Bill's nose. He put yellow, stringy hair over his short red hair.

Next Big Joe put funny ears on Bill and drew a blue mouth from ear to ear. Finally he dressed Bill in the clown suit.

"Now look at yourself," said Big Joe.

Bill looked at himself in surprise.

"Oh!" he said to his uncle, "I look like you! I'm Little Joe!"

"Listen! There's the band!" said Big Joe. "It's time for my first act. Come, Bill. I'll show you where you can watch the circus. I'll call you when it's time for your act."

Bill stood where he could watch the circus and listen to the band without being seen.

The animal acts came first. Lions and the other fierce animals did their acts in big cages.

Soon Big Joe and some other clowns came out and did funny tricks.

Then came fancy horseback riding.

Finally Big Joe came into the ring by himself. This time there was a bright spotlight on him. He was waving his hands and riding a bicycle. Suddenly one of the bicycle wheels fell off.

"Oh!" shouted the crowd. "Look out!" But Big Joe just laughed and bowed.

The funny clown went on riding the one-wheeled bicycle. But now he was standing on his hands and waving his legs in the air as he rode.

Finally Big Joe jumped off the bicycle. He bowed and ran out of the ring as the crowd clapped.

Then a little clown came running out.

"Look!" the people screamed.

"Big Joe is Little Joe now! How did he make himself so small?"

Little Joe started to run around the
ring as the band played faster. Just then
Big Joe came in pushing a baby buggy.

"There's Big Joe!" shouted the crowd.

"There are two of them!"

The big clown and his buggy came
running after the little clown.

Faster and faster they ran.

Faster and faster played the band.

Big Joe finally caught Little Joe and
put him in the buggy. Then he pushed
the buggy out of the ring.

The crowd clapped and clapped until
the two clowns ran out and bowed.

When the circus was over, Big Joe and Little Joe dressed quickly. Outside the tent, they met Mr. and Mrs. Long and Judy. Tom Best and a few other children from school were there, too.

"Here are some of my friends, Uncle Joe," said Bill. "I want them to meet the star clown."

"Bill has told us all about you," said Tom as he shook hands with Big Joe. "I'm certainly glad to meet you. You're a wonderful clown! Little Joe is good, too. Where is he?"

"Oh," said Big Joe, "he's right here. Only you know him as Bill Long."

"Why, Bill!" cried Tom in surprise. "Why didn't you tell us that you were a clown? We thought it was wonderful that your uncle was a circus clown. But having a clown at Maple Grove School is even better!"

Finding a Friend

"I'm not sure I like living here in the country," thought Judy Long while she was feeding her eight baby ducks.

Judy liked the farm animals, and she liked the farm. But she missed all her city friends.

Of course, at the Maple Grove School there were girls she would like to have for friends. But all those girls had been friends for years and years. Judy was not sure they wanted a new friend.

All at once Judy saw Sarah Best come riding by on Dusty.

"Hello," called Sarah.

Judy waved and said, "Hello."

"I'm riding over to Jill Nickel's house," said Sarah.

"Oh, that's nice," said Judy.

She stood watching as Sarah and her pony went on down the road.

"Who was that?" asked Judy's brother.

"Sarah Best," answered Judy. "I wish she had stopped to play with me."

"Sometime you ought to ask her to stop here and visit you," said Bill.

"I don't know Sarah well enough to ask her to stop and play with me," Judy said sadly. "I don't suppose she would want to stop anyway."

"Well," said Bill, "you ought to ask her before you decide she doesn't want to."

"Yes, I suppose I ought to," Judy said as she threw more corn into the pen.

She stood there watching her eight pets as they waddled around picking up corn. Suddenly she laughed and caught one.

"Well," she said, "my ducks like me even if the neighbor girls don't."

Bill shook his head at Judy.

"You're wrong about the girls," he said. "Of course they like you. But you don't act as if you wanted to be friends with them."

"Maybe that's true," Judy said.

When Friday came, she had decided she would invite Sarah to visit her on Saturday.

But when Judy saw Sarah at school, all she asked was, "Do you ride your pony often?"

"Almost every day," said Sarah. "I like my afternoon rides on Dusty."

Then the two girls had to stop talking and start to do their schoolwork.

When Judy got home, her mother asked her if she had invited Sarah to come over to play. Judy shook her head. Then she went out to get a pan of corn to feed her pet ducks.

Judy watched the eight quacking ducks waddle around to get the corn she threw to them. She threw the corn first on one side of the pen and then on the other side.

As Judy watched the ducks waddle from side to side, she heard Dusty's feet coming down the road.

With the pan of corn in her hand, Judy started out toward the road. Suddenly she ran back to the pen. She opened the gate and began to drop corn again.

But this time she did not drop it in the duck pen. She dropped the corn in a straight line from the pen to the road and on across the road.

Then she turned around and started back toward the duck pen, dropping corn all the way. Waddling after Judy was a string of eight ducks, bobbing their heads as they picked up the corn.

The ducks kept bobbing and quacking as they kept following the line of corn. They were right in the middle of the road when Sarah came riding by.

"Whoa, Dusty, whoa," shouted Sarah to her pony. "You had better whoa, or we'll step on all those pretty ducks."

Then Sarah saw Judy. "Hello," she said. "I see that your ducks got out of their pen. That's a smart way to get them back."

"Do you like ducks?" Judy asked.

"Oh, yes," said Sarah. "But we don't have any on our farm. Do you think I could help you feed yours sometime?"

"Why not come tomorrow?" said Judy.

"Fine!" said Sarah. "It's Saturday, and I'll stay all afternoon. Will that be all right?"

"Of course!" said Judy. "But now I'd better get my ducks out of your way."

Judy threw out more corn, and the eight ducks started following her again. Across the road toward their pen they waddled, picking up corn as they went.

Sarah watched until the last duck was inside. Then she waved to Judy and shouted, "See you tomorrow!"

As Judy shut the duck-pen gate, she said, "Well, my little ducks! I hope you didn't mind taking a walk. It was the only way I knew to make a new friend."

Benny's Trick

One afternoon after school there was a funny sight at David Green's farm. David was marching around blowing a horn. Right behind him marched Benny, the young rooster that was his pet.

Toot, toot, David blew on his horn.

"Er-er! Er-roo!" crowed Benny, lifting his head. Then he marched right along behind David.

Every time David blew toot, toot, the rooster crowed, "Er-er! Er-roo!"

Benny had just learned how to do this trick. At first the rooster had not crowed at the right times. But David had kept on trying to teach him the trick. And yesterday Benny had done it right.

David thought it was a funny trick. So he decided to put Benny in the pet show at the Fair in Spring City.

Very early on Saturday morning David heard clucking noises outside. When he looked, he saw a strange truck in the yard. David dressed quickly and went out to see why the truck was there.

Mr. Drew was loading the truck with chickens that David's father had sold to him. There were eight boxes of clucking and squawking chickens.

As the last box was loaded on the truck, David's eyes opened wide. Benny was in a box with the chickens that had been sold!

"Oh, Mr. Drew! Mr. Drew!" screamed David, running to the truck. "Don't take Benny! He's my pet! There's a mistake! There's a mistake!"

But Mr. Drew had climbed up into the truck and was ready to drive away.

Now the engine was making a big noise. David's voice was loud, but the engine was louder.

There was only one thing to do. David had to tell Mr. Drew about Benny before the pet was sold to someone else.

So David made a big jump and caught hold of the back of the truck. Finally he was able to pull himself up into it just before it started.

Away they rode to Spring City. It was not a very long trip, and soon David felt the truck begin to slow down. When it stopped, David was able to jump off.

"Mr. Drew!" shouted David. "There's been an awful mistake! Benny is on your truck. He's my pet rooster. I've been teaching him a trick for the pet parade at the Fair next Tuesday."

"Why, David!" said Mr. Drew. "Which one of these chickens is your pet?"

David pointed and said, "That one. If you'll take him out, I'll show you that he's my pet."

Mr. Drew took the yellow rooster out of the box and put him on the ground.

David pulled the horn out of his pocket. He took a deep breath and began to blow, toot, toot.

He was not sure that Benny would be able to remember his trick. But sure enough, the little rooster crowed, "Er-er! Er-roo!"

Again David blew, toot, toot! And again Benny crowed, "Er-er! Er-roo!"

"That's a funny trick," said Mr. Drew. "I'm sure that chicken is your Benny."

When Mr. Drew counted his load of chickens, he found one too many.

"Why, of course he's yours," Mr. Drew said. "I suppose Benny got into a box last night and was sold by mistake."

"Yes," said David, "but now he can go to the Fair next Tuesday and win a prize. I know he will be the best pet there."

Button-Eyes and the Prize

Jill laughed as Jim's little pig tried to wiggle away. She held on tight to the wet, wiggling pig while Jim rubbed and scrubbed it clean.

Jim was getting Button-Eyes ready for the pet show at the Fair.

At last the fat little pig was washed. After Jim had fastened a bell around the pig's neck, he said, "Oh, look, Jill. Doesn't Button-Eyes look beautiful? She ought to win a prize at the Fair."

On Tuesday the Nickel family went to the Fair. A band was playing, and there was a merry-go-round with all kinds and sizes of animals. Round and round they went—lions, horses, and giraffes.

In one part of the fairground there were ponies to ride for a dime. One little girl was sitting on a white pony that was hitched to the fence. She was waiting to begin her ride.

As Jim and his family walked past, they heard another little girl shout, "I have a dime. I can ride a pony, too!"

When Jim found the place where the pet show was being held, the parade was just about to begin. All kinds and colors and sizes of animals were in the ring.

Jim was near the head of the parade. Behind him waddled Button-Eyes. The bell that was fastened around her neck rang with every step she took.

Ahead of Jim and behind him marched other children with pets.

Up ahead was the rooster that belonged to David Green. Benny crowed loudly as he marched along. In front of him was Easter Bunny. He belonged to Sally Ann Hill, and she held his cage tightly.

Behind the pig was Bobby Sands with his spotted calf. The calf was trying to get away. But Bobby held on tight to the rope and made the calf walk along beside him.

Behind Bobby marched a boy carrying a black crow in a cage. And Dusty was there, hitched to an old wagon.

Next came a girl holding tightly to a gray kitten's cage. Then came Betty Jane with her dog, Hurry, walking quietly and proudly beside her.

What a lot of animals there were—big ones, little ones, and middle-sized ones!

What a lot of noise they made! Squeals, squawks, and grunts filled the air.

Outside the ring a crowd of about a hundred people watched the show.

Three men stood in the middle of the ring to pick out the best-looking and the best-acting pet.

When all the pets had marched around the ring, everyone clapped.

Then one man fastened a blue ribbon on Hurry and said, "This dog wins first prize. He is the best-looking pet, and he knows how to act in a show ring. The blue ribbon belongs to him and his owner, Betty Jane Burns."

"Now!" said the man. "We'll begin the next part of the show to see which pet can do the funniest trick. That pet will win a blue ribbon, too."

"Button-Eyes can't do tricks," thought Jim. "So I'll take her away."

But Jim could not find a way out of the ring. Around he went, with the pig close behind him like a shadow. When Jim slowed down, Button-Eyes slowed down. Her bell rang and rang and rang.

People began to shout at Jim, and his face got as red as fire.

Poor Jim! A hundred people shouting at him!

Then Jim heard the people laughing. He ran around the ring nine times with the pig racing after him.

The people laughed harder and harder.

Poor Jim! A hundred people laughing at him!

He ran until he was out of breath trying to find the way out. At last he saw it right in front of him.

The people laughed harder than ever as the boy and the pig left the ring.

Jim wanted to see who would win the blue ribbon for the funniest trick. So he stood outside the ring to watch.

A pony jumped over a cart. A white goat that was hitched to a red wagon marched once around the ring.

A kitten rolled over and over. A dog went tap, tap on a toy drum. A crow pulled a letter out of a boy's pocket and cried, "Caw! Caw! Caw!"

At last one of the men called to Jim, "Bring your trick pig over here."

Slowly Jim walked back into the ring. Button-Eyes followed right behind him.

"She can't do any tricks," said Jim.

"Oh, we think she can," said the man. "She follows close behind you like a shadow. She runs or walks or stops just when you do. That's a very funny trick."

Then he called out, "This pig wins the blue ribbon for the funniest trick. She belongs to Jim Nickel."

All the people clapped and clapped.

Happy Jim! A hundred people clapping for him!

How Tom Went to the Fair

It was the second day of the Fair—the day of the airplane races. How Tom and Sarah wanted to see those races!

The races would not begin until noon, but the children wanted to be there by ten o'clock.

After breakfast the family hurried to do the farm work. So they were able to start between nine and ten o'clock.

But as they drove by their pasture, Mr. Best said, "Look at that! The cows are out of the pasture. I'll have to drive them back and fix the fence."

"Oh, Father!" cried Sarah. "Can't we go to the Fair first and see the races?"

Before Mr. Best could answer, Tom said, "I'll drive the cows back and fix the fence. I know how to fix it."

"The airplane races begin at noon!" cried Sarah. "You'll miss them."

"Oh, no," said Tom. "When I finish the fence, I'll walk to Uncle Zeke's and get a ride. It's only half a mile."

"Well, here's your Fair ticket," said Tom's father. "We'll meet at the airfield. Uncle Zeke is starting between eleven and half-past eleven. I'm sure you can fix the fence in time to get there."

Tom got out of the car and watched the family ride off.

Before he could begin to fix the fence, he had to drive the cows back into the pasture. That was not easy.

"Moo! Moo! Moo!" went the cows. They wanted to stay outside, and it was a long time before Tom finished driving them into the pasture.

He put the boards across the fence and went to get nails and a hammer. By the time he got back to the pasture, he knew it was getting late. The sun was higher, and the shadows were getting shorter.

But Tom could not quit now. He had to nail the boards in place.

"It must be half-past eleven already," Tom thought when he finished. "By this time Uncle Zeke and Aunt Kitty have left for the Fair."

Poor Tom. How he hated to miss the airplane races! He picked up the hammer and the nails that were left. Then he started slowly to the house. No use hurrying now. It was already too late to go with Uncle Zeke and Aunt Kitty.

All at once Tom heard the sound of an airplane. It flew in a circle above him. Finally it came almost straight down and landed in the pasture.

Tom could hardly believe his eyes.

Dropping the hammer and nails, he raced toward the strange-looking plane.

Tom knew the man who stepped out. It was Mr. White. He had sold Tom's father a new farm machine.

"Hello, Tom," Mr. White said. "I was circling around over your farm when I saw you down here. I thought you were all going to the airplane races today."

Tom said, "My family will be there. They started early this morning, between nine and ten o'clock."

"You had better get started, too," said Mr. White. "The Fair is more than twenty miles north of here. It's half-past eleven, and the airplane races start at noon."

"Yes, I know," said Tom, "but we had some bad luck." Then he told Mr. White about the pasture fence.

"Now I can't use my Fair ticket," Tom said sadly. "After I finished the fence, I was going to walk a half mile north and ride with Uncle Zeke. But I know he has already started, and I can't walk twenty-nine miles."

"Well," said Mr. White, "I think we can turn your bad luck into good luck. Hop in. I'll take you to the airplane races myself. We can fly twenty-nine miles quicker than you can walk one half a mile."

Tom was so excited that he could not say a word. He just climbed in.

Mr. White started the engine, and Tom felt himself going straight up off the ground. High above the pasture they rose, and then they headed north.

The roads below looked like ribbons between the green fields. The horses and cows down below looked like little toys, and so did the houses and barns.

The twenty-nine miles to the Fair seemed like one. Soon Tom and Mr. White were circling above the fairground. Tom saw the people below hurrying about like busy little bugs.

He knew that he was dropping lower and lower now. The people down below were beginning to look larger and larger.

Tom saw hundreds of people looking up to watch them land. As they dropped lower, Tom thought he could see people he knew.

When they landed, Tom jumped out. Standing near the high fence were his mother, father, and sister.

"I'm here," Tom shouted to them. "I got to the airplane races in time!"

"You certainly did," said his father proudly. "But we didn't think you would fly here!"

The Traveling Christmas Party

Maple Grove School was getting ready for a Christmas party.

The children trimmed their tree with ropes of silver and glass balls of different sizes. They hung stars on the tree and put the biggest star on top.

Everyone was wishing that Bill and Judy Long could see the tree, too. They were the only children who were not at school today.

"Mrs. Long telephoned this morning," said Miss Valentine. "She said Judy and Bill won't be well enough to come to school for about eight days. So they can't come to the party on Friday."

For a few seconds every child was so quiet you could have heard a pin drop.

Suddenly Sarah said, "Then let's take the Christmas party to them!"

"How?" asked the other children.

Then Sarah told them her plan. She asked everyone to keep it a secret so that it would be a surprise for Bill and Judy.

At last it was Friday afternoon and time for the Christmas party. All the neighbors from the different farms were coming.

When Mr. Best and his wife drove up, Tom and Sarah were not with them. But the other children knew that they were working on the secret plan.

About twenty minutes later, Tom and Sarah came riding up on a big sled with Dusty hitched to it.

As Tom tied Dusty to a tree, Jim ran out and asked, "Is everything ready?"

"Yes," said Tom. "Let's go inside."

How pretty the schoolroom looked! The walls were trimmed with holly and green branches tied with red ribbon.

On the desk was the Christmas tree. A big sign on the wall above the desk said "Merry Christmas to All."

After everyone had sat down, Miss Valentine read a beautiful Christmas story. "Now," she said, "it's time for someone else to visit our party."

Near the back wall there was a big chimney made of red paper. Suddenly there was a sound of bells. Then out of the chimney came a jolly Santa Claus who wore a red suit and a red cap.

"Hello, Santa Claus!" the people cried, but everybody thought he looked like Mr. Burns.

"Merry Christmas," said Santa as he opened a bag of presents. He drew out a paintbox, a drawing book, a puzzle, a doll, a box of writing paper, and a fancy pin.

Still the bag was half full. Then Santa Claus drew out more presents. A bunch of balloons, a toy bus, five balls of different sizes, and a tiny wooden horse.

There was a present for each child.

When the last child had the last gift, everyone had some chocolate ice cream and Christmas cookies. Fruit, nuts, and chocolate candy were passed around, too.

Then Sarah told about the secret plan.

"We are going to move the Christmas party to Judy and Bill," she said. "Dusty can take the tree on our sled."

"That's a fine plan!" said Santa Claus. "A traveling Christmas party!"

He raised the tree from the desk and carried it to the sled outside. Tom helped him nail the tree to the sled so that it would not fall over.

In a circle under the tree they put gifts for Bill and Judy. There were bags of fruit, nuts, and chocolate candy. There was a sailboat, a jumping jack, and a big bunch of holly.

Santa Claus shouted, "Go ahead. The rest of us will come later in our cars."

The secret Christmas party was soon on
its way. Tom led the pony while Don
walked along beside the tree to see that
it did not fall over.

Dusty looked very gay. His head was
trimmed with red ribbon. A bunch of
holly was fastened between his ears.

A child had hung a bunch of silver bells
underneath Dusty's ears. The bells rang
out with a merry sound as Tom led the
pony along the snowy road.

After a while Sarah drove up to the house where Bill and Judy Long lived. Tom led Dusty right up to the porch. "Whoa, Dusty!" he said. "Whoa!"

Then the automobiles came driving up with Santa Claus and all the people.

Mrs. Long saw them through the window and ran to get Judy and Bill.

Very soon the two children were at the window. How excited they were!

A Christmas tree had come traveling up to their door! A beautiful Christmas tree—all silver and red and green!

In his jolly voice Santa Claus called out, "Let's all sing a song for Judy and Bill."

Everyone sang a gay song as Santa led the singing in his big, deep voice.

"Jingle bells, jingle bells,
Jingle all the way."

Just then Dusty shook his head, and the bells underneath his ears rang out. Jingle, jingle, jingle!

"Oh!" laughed Sarah. "Hear Dusty's bells go jingle, jingle! He's helping us with our song."

Tom went to the window and held
up the sailboat for Bill to see. Sarah held
up Judy's jumping jack.

Santa Claus lifted the tree from the
sled and put it on the porch. Don took
out the bags of chocolate candy and fruit
and nuts. He placed the gifts in a circle
underneath the tree.

Mr. Long came out on the porch and
thanked all the people. Then he took
the tree and the gifts into the house.

Judy and Bill were very happy. They
could not go to the party at school, but
the Christmas party had traveled to them.

On the Road
to Storyland

A Ride to Animal Town

One day Billy Beaver was riding to Animal Town. Johnny Fox was hitched to his wooden cart. The day was warm, and Johnny Fox walked along slowly.

All at once Billy Beaver saw a tired old bunny by the side of the road.

"Whoa, Johnny!" Billy called. "Whoa!"

Then he said to the bunny, "If you are going to Animal Town, hop in!"

Without saying a word, the tired old bunny picked up his red jacket and hopped into the cart.

After a little while the old rabbit said something very soft and low.

"What did you say?" asked Billy.

"Oh, nothing."

"Yes, you did. You said something."

"Oh, I just said that your wooden cart is hard to sit on."

"Then put your jacket under you."

The tired old rabbit sat on his jacket. They went on a little farther. Then the rabbit said something again. He said it very soft and low.

"What did you say?" Billy asked.

"Oh, nothing. Nothing at all."

"Yes, you did. I heard you."

"Oh, I just said that Johnny Fox goes very slowly."

"Johnny Fox is doing the best he can," said Billy Beaver. "The sun is hot, and he has gone three miles already."

"Oh," said the rabbit.

They went on farther, past a yellow
house and a pretty garden.

By and by the tired old bunny began
to grumble again. He said something
very soft and low.

"What did you say?" asked Billy.

"Oh, nothing."

"Yes, you did," said Billy Beaver. "I
heard you grumbling."

"I just said that I can't see what is
in front of us. You're so wide."

"I can't help being wide," said Billy.
"Beavers are always wide."

Johnny Fox went on and on. After a while he came to a large wooden bridge. Bumpety-bumpety-bump went the wheels of the cart, and the tired old bunny grumbled again.

"What did you say this time?" asked Billy Beaver.

"Oh, nothing."

"Yes, you did. I heard you grumbling."

"Well, I just said that this bridge underneath us is bumpy. It shakes me all around and hurts my tail."

Billy Beaver called, "Whoa! Whoa, there!" Then he looked around at the old rabbit.

"Better get out, Rabbit," he said.

"Get out!" said the rabbit. "Why?"

"If you don't like to ride, you can get out and walk," answered Billy.

"But I do like to ride," said the tired rabbit, staying right where he was.

"You don't behave as if you liked it," said Billy Beaver. "You keep grumbling and saying things very soft and low.

"You said that this wooden cart is hard to sit on. You said that Johnny Fox goes slowly. You said that you can't see what is in front of you.

"And now you say that this bridge underneath us is bumpy and shakes you. Better get out, Rabbit. Better get out and walk."

The rabbit looked at Billy Beaver. Then he hopped down and began to walk along the hot road, carrying his jacket.

The cart went along farther—past a big red barn and over another bridge.

As the rabbit walked along behind the cart, he got hotter and hotter. He took a handkerchief out of his jacket pocket and rubbed his face. At last he said something very soft and low.

"What did you say?" asked Billy.

"I said, 'Let me get in and try again.' "

"Whoa," said Billy Beaver. "Whoa!"

He thought a little while, and then he said, "All right. Get in."

The tired old bunny got in, but he did not say a word.

After a long time the old rabbit said something very soft and low.

"Now you're grumbling again," said Billy Beaver. "What did you say?"

"I said, 'Hot sun, bumpy road, tired old feet. Glad to ride.'"

"Oh," said Billy Beaver. "Is that what you said? Now say one thing more."

"What?"

"Think it over, Rabbit."

Farther and farther they went along the bumpy road. Bumpety-bump!

At last the tired old bunny rabbit said something. "Glad to ride," he said. "THANK YOU!"

"That is polite," said Billy Beaver. "You are welcome, Rabbit! YOU'RE VERY WELCOME!"

Then Billy Beaver and the tired old bunny rode on to Animal Town.

Tippy Elephant's Hat

Tippy's Naughty Tricks

Tippy Elephant was a circus baby.

"Why do you call me Tippy?" she asked her mother one day.

"Because you tip around so," said her mother. "You put your front feet down so hard that you tip up behind. Then you put your back feet down so hard that you tip up in front."

"I like tipping back and forth," said the frisky little elephant.

131

What Tippy liked best was to stamp hard with her right front foot.

One afternoon she saw a little boy's balloon and stamped on it. Smash!

"Oh, Tippy!" said Mrs. Elephant. "I wish you would stop being so naughty. I wish you would behave yourself."

"I don't want to behave myself," said Tippy. "It's more fun to be frisky."

Then she saw a pail of water. Splash went her frisky front foot into the pail. The little elephant could not behave herself for even a minute.

The next minute naughty little Tippy reached out her trunk and snatched a straw hat from a man's head. Then she dropped the hat on the ground and stamped on it with her frisky foot.

"You are a naughty, naughty child!" cried Mrs. Elephant, shaking her head.

Almost every day a man at the circus would give Tippy some peanuts or an apple. First she would bow to him like a polite little elephant. Then she would snatch the man's hat with her trunk.

Stamp, stamp! She would smash the hat with her frisky front foot. One day she smashed eleven different hats.

At last one of the circus men said,
"We'll have to sell that naughty little
elephant if she doesn't behave better."

"Did you hear that?" Mrs. Elephant
said to her child. "You'll have to learn
to behave better, or the man will sell
you. You'll have to stop smashing hats,
or you can't travel with this circus."

"But I love to be frisky!" cried the
naughty Tippy. Then she snatched three
more hats and smashed them flat.

Tippy Learns a Lesson

One afternoon Tippy said to herself, "Boys and girls often come to see me. Why can't I go to visit some of them?"

Off she went tipping across a hayfield. In her way was a shiny tin can, but her frisky foot smashed it flat.

In a yard she saw a girl and a boy. They were digging in a sandbox under a big colored umbrella. They each had a shiny tin pail and a tin shovel.

Tippy walked right into the yard.

"Run, Molly, run!" shouted the boy. Both children threw their shiny tin pails down in the sand. They threw their tin shovels down, too, and ran to the porch.

Then Tippy lifted her frisky foot and knocked down the umbrella.

Next she smashed the shiny tin pails. Bang! Bang! She smashed them both as flat as she could.

"Please stop!" said the little boy. "If you'll stop spoiling our toys, I'll give you some peanuts."

He ran inside the house and got a big bag of peanuts. Tippy stepped up to the porch and took a peanut from the boy's hand with her trunk. When she had eaten it, she made a polite bow.

"Oh, you're thanking us," said Molly. "You're welcome, Baby Elephant! You're very welcome!"

As Tippy took each peanut, she made a polite bow. Molly kept saying, "You're welcome." But when naughty Tippy had eaten all the peanuts, she smashed the girl's tin shovel as flat as she could.

"Please stop!" said Molly. "If you'll stop, I'll give you a lovely present."

Molly hurried into the house and got an old straw hat that was trimmed with a big pink flower.

Tippy put her head down low while Molly tied the old hat on. Then Tippy made a polite bow and went tipping off to show her fancy hat to her mother.

"Tippy, how sweet you look in that lovely hat!" said Mrs. Elephant. Then she called to the giraffe, "Oh, Mr. Giraffe! Come and see Tippy's lovely hat."

Tippy bowed her head to show the giraffe how lovely the hat was.

The giraffe put his head down low to smell the pretty flower. Two monkeys came to look at the hat, too.

One of the circus men heard about Tippy's lovely hat and came to see it. The baby elephant reached out her trunk and snatched the man's hat.

Just as she threw it down on the ground, a funny thing happened.

Tippy's own hat fell off.

Smash! Her frisky front foot landed on her own hat and smashed it flat.

"Oh, oh, oh!" cried the unhappy little elephant. "My hat with the lovely pink flower is spoiled! It's smashed flat."

The man, the giraffe, the monkeys, and Mrs. Elephant felt sorry for Tippy.

"It's too bad that your lovely hat is spoiled," said the giraffe.

Mrs. Elephant said, "I'm sorry your hat is spoiled. But you have learned a lesson. Now you know how unhappy the men felt when you spoiled their hats."

"Yes, I've learned my lesson," said Tippy. "I'll never stamp on any more hats or balloons or tin pails. Never!"

And she never did.

Sojo

Sojo's Bright Idea

Sojo was a little boy who was always very, very sleepy.

One morning his mother called him.

"Wake up," she said. "After breakfast I want you to water the cabbage plants."

After Sojo had eaten his breakfast of sweet porridge and milk, he started to the pond to get some water.

When he was almost there, Sojo lay down underneath a tree to rest. Pretty soon he was fast asleep.

After a while Sojo woke up from his
nap because he heard a splashing noise.
At the pond he saw a small elephant
splashing water with his trunk.

"It must be fun to do that," said Sojo,
opening his mouth in a big yawn.

"It isn't very much fun," said the little
elephant. "It's too easy."

Then Sojo remembered the cabbages
that needed watering, and suddenly he
had a bright idea.

"I know a place where splashing would
be fun," he said. "But it would be too
hard to splash there. You wouldn't be
able to do it. You are too small."

"Pooh!" shouted the elephant. "I can splash anywhere. Show me the place."

The elephant begged and begged.

At last the mischievous little boy said, "Since you're a friend of mine, I don't want you to be unhappy. Fill your trunk with water and follow me.

"This is a new game," Sojo said. "You must sprinkle the water carefully on the cabbages. If you sprinkle all the rows just right, you get four points and win the game. You see, it's a hard game."

"Pooh," said the elephant as he began to sprinkle the first row of cabbages. "This isn't hard. It's easy."

The elephant sprinkled water on all the green cabbages in the garden. The mischievous Sojo sat and watched.

At last the elephant said, "Now I've sprinkled water on all four rows. Does that count four points?"

"No," said Sojo. "You made a mistake and sprinkled too fast on one row."

"Please, won't you let me try again?" begged the little elephant.

"Well," said Sojo, "you're a friend of mine, and I hate to see you unhappy. Try again on Friday."

"Oh, thank you," said the elephant.

"You're welcome," Sojo answered with a mischievous smile. Then he yawned and lay down in the shade. In a moment he was sound asleep.

When his mother woke him for lunch, she was surprised to see how well the cabbage plants had been watered.

Sojo's Second Bright Idea

After lunch Sojo's mother said, "Now I want you to cut the grass on the path."

Sojo went out, but he did not cut the grass. He lay down in the cool shade underneath a tree and fell asleep.

When he woke up from his nap, he saw a goat eating grass near the path.

Then Sojo had another bright idea.

"Hello!" he said with a yawn. "Don't you know you mustn't eat that grass?"

"Why not?" asked the goat.

"Because it doesn't belong to you. It belongs to us," said Sojo.

"Now, Sojo, be a good fellow," begged the goat. "Let me eat just a little."

"Well," said Sojo, "you are a friend of mine, and I hate to see you unhappy. I'll let you eat the grass on the path."

Then the mischievous fellow went back to sleep in the shade.

When Sojo woke up, the goat had eaten all the grass on the path. He begged Sojo to let him eat more grass.

"Not now," said Sojo. "But come back next Tuesday. There will be more grass on the path then."

"Oh, thank you," said the goat.

"You're welcome," yawned Sojo, and in a moment he was asleep again.

When Sojo's mother woke him from his nap, she was surprised to see how well the grass had been cut.

Sojo's Third Bright Idea

After Sojo had finished his supper, he went to bed. He looked for Brown Bird, who came to the window every evening and sang until Sojo was asleep.

But this evening Brown Bird did not come. Sojo thought he could not sleep until Brown Bird came to sing for him.

In a few moments a different bird with lovely red feathers came and began to sing a soft, sweet song.

Again mischievous Sojo had an idea.

"Hello, Red Bird!" he called. "If you tried, maybe you could sing almost as well as Brown Bird."

"What is so wonderful about that fellow's song?" asked Red Bird.

"Well," said Sojo, "he can sing for an hour without stopping. Your song is sweet, but it's too short. You can't sing for a whole hour."

"Pooh!" said Red Bird with a flap of his wings. "I can, too! I can sing longer than an hour."

He opened his mouth and sang and sang and sang.

"That's a good song," said Sojo with a yawn. "Very—good—." After a moment Sojo did not say anything more.

When Red Bird had finished, he said, "Is my song as good as Brown Bird's?"

But he never did find out what Sojo thought because Sojo was sound asleep.

Noisy Mr. Redhead

In the woods there was an old, old tree that stood on the bank of a river. That was where Mrs. Frisky and her six babies had their home. They lived in a hole in a limb of the old tree.

Mrs. Frisky was a gray squirrel with a long, beautiful tail. Her babies were pretty, too. Mrs. Frisky loved those six babies more than anything else in the world.

From *Martin the Goose Boy*, by Marie Barringer. Copyright, 1932, by Marie Barringer, reprinted by permission of Doubleday & Company, Inc.

Too-oo was a wise old owl who had her nest in the trunk of the same tree. The owl was such a good neighbor that the squirrels all loved her.

Too-oo was kind and pleasant and very polite. She never made a loud noise or bothered anybody. In the daytime she was always asleep, and in the evening she always flew off to hunt food.

One day a stranger came to live in
the old tree. He was Mr. Redhead, the
woodpecker. He was a noisy neighbor,
always bothering Mrs. Frisky with his
hammering.

Tick-tack, tick-tack-tack! His drumming
noise kept up all day as he hunted food in
the limbs of the trees.

One afternoon when he was drumming
hard, the owl woke up and rushed out.

"That's a terrible noise!" she grumbled
to Mrs. Frisky. "The wrens and the
robins don't bother us with such awful
noises. I hate to complain, but I wish
that we could get rid of Mr. Redhead."

"So do I," said Mrs. Frisky. "I don't want my babies to be bothered by his awful noise."

"How in the world can I sleep?" the owl complained with an angry flap of her wings. "I can't get even a nap. I'll hunt for a new home right now."

Away she flew.

Just then Mrs. Frisky saw two boys walking along the path by the river. From a high limb she watched them stop underneath her tree. The boys made a big fire of dry sticks and began to bake some potatoes.

Mrs. Frisky did not like to see flames and smoke so close to the dry old tree. She watched until the boys had eaten their lunch and had stamped on the fire to put it out.

After they left, Mrs. Frisky felt safe. She and her babies went to sleep.

But Mr. Redhead was still watching.

He saw a little smoke and some tiny orange flames. Then the orange flames spread to the dry old tree. In a moment smoke was coming out of the owl's door.

Mr. Redhead flew to Mrs. Frisky's door and hammered just as hard as he could. Tick-tack, tick-tack! It was the loudest noise he had ever made.

It woke Mrs. Frisky, who rushed to the door scolding and complaining.

But when she got there, she was too scared to scold. Smoke was coming out of the hole where the owl lived. Mrs. Frisky knew that her own home would be full of smoke in a minute.

She rushed inside and shook her babies to wake them. She pushed them through the doorway and led them out to a limb of another tree.

Too-oo, the owl, was still out in the forest hunting for a new nest. When she saw the smoke, she came flying back to find out what was happening.

Just then orange flames roared up the trunk and limbs of the dry old tree.

Mrs. Frisky was afraid the flames would spread over the whole forest. But then she felt a sprinkle of rain.

After the first sprinkle, the rain began to pour down. It poured and poured so hard that it soon put out all the flames and kept the fire from spreading.

"The flames are out!" Mrs. Frisky called to Mr. Redhead, who was sitting on a nearby limb. "Thank you for saving us from being burned by the flames.

"You are the best neighbor in the whole world, and I hope you'll always be our neighbor."

That evening the owl found a tree where they could all make their homes.

After that Mr. Redhead's noise never bothered Too-oo or Mrs. Frisky. When they heard his tick-tack, they would say, "There's Mr. Redhead! The very best neighbor in the whole world!"

The Story of White Satin

Once upon a time there was a white pony who was as smooth and shiny as satin. So he was called White Satin.

He belonged to Farmer Gay. Every morning he was hitched to a fancy buggy. Then he would take Farmer Gay's little girl, Sally Ann, for a ride.

"I am the most beautiful pony in the world," he thought as he trotted along, drawing the red buggy behind him.

He was a very foolish pony—always thinking about himself.

But early one morning the pony saw
something new outside his barn.

It was smooth and shiny, too. It was
as blue as the sky, and it was trimmed
with silver bands. It was a beautiful
sky-blue automobile.

When he saw it, the foolish pony
became very cross. He put his ears back,
showed his teeth, stamped his feet, and
began to grumble to himself.

When Farmer Gay's little girl came into the yard, she did not even look at White Satin. She just looked at the sky-blue car with its silver bands and said, "Isn't it beautiful! It's as smooth and shiny as satin."

"That's not true," scolded the angry pony. "How foolish she is to call that ugly car beautiful! I am the one who is as smooth and shiny as satin! I am the one who is beautiful!"

Then Farmer Gay spoke to his little girl. "Let's take a ride," he said.

The pony thought, "She doesn't love that ugly car. She won't get into it. She loves me. She certainly will hitch me to my buggy and drive me."

But he was wrong. The little girl did not hitch him to the buggy. She got into the blue car with her father and rode away.

The pony was as cross as he could be. He stamped his feet and showed his big teeth.

"They didn't even speak to me," he grumbled. "I won't stay here. I'll run away, and then they'll be sorry."

While the family was eating supper, the foolish pony rushed out of the barn and galloped away.

On he galloped, past wheat fields and pastures, until he came to a pond at the bottom of a hill. He wanted a drink. So he leaped right in.

He landed in the pond with a big splash and woke up the frogs who lived there. All together they began to make a great noise.

"Better get out! Better get out!" croaked the grandfather frogs in their low, gruff voices. "Better get out! Better get out!"

"Too deep! Too deep!" croaked the father frogs. "Too deep! Too deep!"

"Leap, leap! Leap, leap!" squeaked the younger frogs in their little high voices. "Leap, leap! Leap, leap!"

White Satin tried to leap out, but he could not. His feet were stuck fast in the mud at the bottom of the pond. The harder he tried to get out, the deeper he went into the mud. He could not pull even one foot out of the sticky mud.

Then he heard the frogs again.

"He'll never get out! He'll never get out!" croaked the grandfather frogs in their low, gruff voices.

"Going deeper! Going deeper!" croaked the father frogs.

"Too late to leap! Too late to leap!" squeaked the little frogs.

White Satin was afraid that the frogs were right. His feet were going deeper and deeper into the sticky mud at the bottom of the pond.

The pony was not cross now. He was scared and unhappy. He had never been so unhappy in all his life.

White Satin began to scream for help.

After a while a farmer heard him and came to the pond. The man looked at the pony and then rushed off. He was going to telephone Farmer Gay, but the poor unhappy pony did not know that.

"He isn't going to help me," thought the pony. "He didn't even speak to me. I'll never get off the bottom of this cold pond."

White Satin felt worse and worse. He was so unhappy that big tears ran down his nose and dropped into the water.

As the pony got colder and colder, he felt worse and worse. The tears ran down his face faster and faster.

At last he heard a car rolling up to the pond.

In the front seat sat Farmer Gay and his little girl. In the back seat was the farmer who had found White Satin. Quickly the two men got out.

The frogs were croaking again.

"Too late! Too late!" they croaked.

"He'll never get out! He'll never get out!"

"He's in too deep! He's in too deep!"

"Maybe they are right," thought the pony as more tears splashed into the water. "I'll never see my nice, warm barn or my green pasture again."

But Farmer Gay called to him, "Don't be afraid, White Satin. We'll pull you out with the new car."

First they threw logs onto the mud. Over the logs they put boards. Next Farmer Gay walked out on the boards and hitched a rope around the pony. He tied the other end of the rope to the car.

Then the car backed up and pulled. Slowly the pony's front feet and then his hind feet were pulled out of the mud.

He was not smooth and shiny now. He was covered with mud. His teeth were chattering from the cold, and tears were running down his face.

The frogs began to croak again.

"Better go home! Better go home!"

"And get to bed! And get to bed!"

"And go to sleep! And go to sleep!"

That was just what poor, tired White Satin wanted to do. But first he went up to the blue car with the silver bands.

He was not cross now. He did not put his ears back or stamp his feet or show his teeth. Instead, he rubbed his nose against the automobile.

Now White Satin loved the sky-blue car. It had saved his life.

Brother Rabbit and Tar Baby

Brother Fox certainly did want to catch Brother Rabbit. The fox had tried many different tricks, but he had never been able to catch the rabbit.

One day Brother Fox tried a new trick. He got a doll and a pail of soft black tar. He set the doll in the middle of the road and covered it smoothly with plenty of sticky tar.

"This Tar Baby is the best trick I ever thought of in my life," he said with a wicked laugh.

Then Brother Fox hid in some bushes close by. He waited and watched.

By and by Brother Rabbit came down the road. When he saw Tar Baby, he stood right up on his long hind legs in surprise.

Then he spoke to Tar Baby. "Good morning!" he said. "Nice weather we're having."

Tar Baby did not say a word.

"Is that the way to behave?" grumbled Brother Rabbit. "I spoke to you, and you had better speak to me. Can't you hear what I'm saying? If you can't, I'll talk a little louder."

Tar Baby did not say a word.

"You're a stuck-up fellow. That's what you are," shouted Brother Rabbit. "Speak to me, or I'll hit you. And I can hit hard. Now are you going to speak?"

Tar Baby did not say a word.

"I'll teach you a lesson you won't forget," said Brother Rabbit. Raising his left front foot, he hit Tar Baby hard.

Of course his foot stuck tight in the tar, and he could not get it loose.

"Let me loose," screamed the foolish rabbit. "If you don't, I'll hit you much harder."

Tar Baby did not say a word. So the rabbit hit Tar Baby with his right front foot. And of course that foot also stuck.

Next the rabbit hit Tar Baby with both hind feet, and they stuck. Finally he bumped his head hard against Tar Baby. Then his head stuck also.

Brother Fox came out from the bushes, prancing along as pleased as could be. He certainly was enjoying himself.

"Good morning," he called. "So you think Tar Baby is a stuck-up fellow! It seems to me you're the one that's stuck up. All stuck up with tar!"

The fox laughed wickedly, "Ho, ho, ho!"

He laughed so hard that he rolled on the ground, with tears running down his face. He certainly was enjoying himself.

"Dear, kind Brother Fox!" begged the poor rabbit. "Please pull me loose."

"Oh, no!" said the wicked old fox. "I won't pull you loose. I'll cook you, and I'll roast you, and I'll eat you for my dinner!"

"Oh, Brother Fox," begged the rabbit with tears in his eyes. "Please don't eat me. Eat something else instead."

"I don't want anything else," said the fox with his wicked smile. "I can hardly wait for my first bite of roast rabbit!"

The fox raked a big pile of leaves over a log close to Tar Baby. Then he set the pile on fire to cook the rabbit.

As the fire burned, Brother Rabbit got hotter and hotter. He had never been so hot in all his life. He turned and twisted and twisted and turned, trying to get away from the smoke and the flames.

Suddenly Brother Rabbit felt his head pulling loose from Tar Baby. The hot fire was making the tar soft.

Then Brother Rabbit had a bright idea. He thought, "My head is already loose. Maybe I can also pull my feet loose if the tar grows softer. But first I'll get rid of the fox so that he can't see me."

So the rabbit grumbled and scolded. "Brother Fox," he said, "you can't roast me with this tiny fire. You need a great big fire instead of this little one."

"All right," said the fox. "I'll bring plenty of logs and make a bigger fire. I'll roast you nice and brown."

As soon as Brother Fox had pranced off, Brother Rabbit began to twist and turn some more. He twisted and turned and turned and twisted until he pulled his hind feet loose.

When his hind feet were loose, he twisted and turned and turned and twisted until his front feet were loose. Then away he hopped.

The rabbit hid in some bushes where he was safe from the smoke and flames.

"Ho, ho, ho!" he called out. "I have spoiled your plans, Brother Fox. Build your fire big and hot, but what will you have to cook? You can cook, and you can roast, but you won't have any roast rabbit for dinner!"

Off to his home went Brother Rabbit. As he hopped along, he was laughing about the way he had fooled Brother Fox.

He certainly was enjoying himself.

Paddy's Christmas

One winter day Paddy Bear watched some children through a window of a log cabin. As Paddy watched, he saw exciting things. He heard exciting things. He smelled exciting things.

The children were very happy and gay.

"Merry Christmas," they called.

"So it's Christmas that makes people happy and gay," said Paddy to himself. "I wonder what Christmas is."

Then the little bear left the cabin and started back to his home on a high mountain.

He hurried up the mountain to the big, dark cave where he lived.

"What is Christmas?" he asked his father, his mother, his uncle, and his aunt. But the grown-up bears were sound asleep and did not hear Paddy. He poked them and bumped up against them until they woke up.

He said, "The children in the log cabin at the foot of the mountain are having Christmas. What is Christmas?"

"I don't know," yawned Father Bear.

"I don't know," yawned mother Bear.

"We don't know," yawned Aunt Bear and Uncle Bear. "Don't bother us."

All the big bears went back to sleep.

Once more Paddy bumped up against the grown-up bears. At last Uncle Bear woke up. "I'll go down the mountain," he said with a big yawn. "I'll find out what Christmas is."

Down to the foot of the steep mountain went Uncle Bear. He hid behind the log cabin and listened and looked and sniffed. Then he climbed up to his cave.

"Christmas is evergreen trees and holly," he said to little Paddy. "You get them and trim your house. Then you sing a song, and that is Christmas."

Uncle Bear went back to sleep. But the little cub ran out of the cave. He got a little evergreen tree and some holly with red berries on it to trim the cave.

He set the tree in the cave and nailed the holly on the walls. Then he sang a song and pranced around the cave, and for a while he was happy.

But soon Paddy began to feel that something was wrong. "This isn't Christmas," said the little cub, shaking his head. "Uncle Bear must be wrong. Christmas surely is something more than evergreen trees and holly."

Once more he called the grown-up bears. When they did not wake up, the little cub poked them with his paws. First he gave them a small poke, then a harder poke. Next he bumped up against them, and at last the big bears woke up.

"This isn't Christmas," said Paddy. "When children have Christmas, they get all sorts of pretty things and have lots of fun. They feel good from the inside out. My holly and my evergreen tree look pretty, and I'm having lots of fun. But I don't feel good from the inside out."

This time it was Aunt Bear who said she would find out what Christmas is.

Down went Aunt Bear to the cabin at the foot of the steep mountain. She hid behind the cabin and listened and looked.

When she got back to the cave, she said, "Christmas is getting all sorts of gifts, like toys and things to eat. You play and have a good time. Look! I've brought you some gifts, Paddy."

In one big paw she had a string of red berries for the cub. In another paw she had a small piece of log full of honey. She gave Paddy the berries and the honey. Then she went back to sleep.

Paddy hung the string of red berries around his neck. He gobbled up the honey and pranced around the cave, and for a while he was happy.

But soon the cub began to feel that something was wrong.

He thought and thought about it.

At last he called the grown-up bears again. When they did not wake up, Paddy poked them with his paws and bumped against them. At last he woke them.

Paddy said, "This still doesn't feel like Christmas. When girls and boys have Christmas, they get all sorts of pretty things. They have lots of fun, and they feel good from the inside out."

Then in a puzzled voice the cub said, "The string of red berries is very pretty, and the honey tasted good. I'm having lots of fun, but I don't feel good from the inside out. So Aunt Bear must be wrong. Christmas must be something more than getting presents."

Mother Bear stood up. "I'll go and find out what Christmas is," she said.

Down went Mother Bear to the cabin at the foot of the steep mountain. She hid behind the cabin for a long time and looked and listened and sniffed.

When she got back to the cave, she said, "I have found out what Christmas is! It is more than evergreen trees and holly with pretty red berries. And it is more than getting presents. It is doing something to make someone else happy." Then she went to sleep again.

Paddy ran to the woods at once.

Soon he came prancing back to the cave. His paws were loaded with all sorts of gifts for the grown-up bears.

Once more Paddy poked and bumped the grown-up bears until he woke them.

"Merry Christmas!" Paddy cried. He gave Mother Bear a big bunch of branches to clean the cave with. He gave Father Bear a stick to lean on when he climbed the steep mountain.

Paddy's gift to Uncle Bear was a big bag of nuts. And for Aunt Bear he had three red feathers in a basket.

Then Paddy knew that it was really Christmas, for suddenly he felt good from the inside out.

Miss Molly Squeak

Grandmother Page liked to rock. So when she came to Billy's house, she brought her rocking chair. It had been made by Great-Grandfather Page more than one hundred years ago.

Father Page put the rocking chair in the warmest place in the house.

Soon Grandmother Page sat down and started to rock Baby Janey to sleep.

Billy stood by, almost wishing that he were a baby so that he could be rocked.

"Stand on the rocker, Billy," said Grandmother. "Then we can all rock."

So Billy stood on the rocker and leaned against the chair back. Grandmother rocked back and forth, back and forth.

"Listen, the chair is talking," said Billy. "Hear it say, 'Squeak, squeak.'"

"Yes," said Grandmother. "That is my friend, Miss Molly Squeak. She has lived in my chair ever since it was made."

"How do you suppose she got in?" asked Billy.

"Oh, that's easy," said Grandmother Page. "Molly found an empty place where two pieces of wood had been joined together. All the Squeak family love to live in places like that."

"The Squeak family!" said Billy. "Is there a whole family of them?"

"Oh, my, yes!" Grandmother Page said. "And a noisy family it is, too."

All this time Molly had been singing, "Squeak, squeak, squeak, squeak."

One rainy day the old rocker was left out on the porch. The wooden chair got very wet, and the pieces of wood in it began to grow bigger. Soon the loose places where the wood was joined together became smaller.

At last Molly Squeak's hiding place grew so small that she was pushed out of it.

She hurried into the house and looked for a new place to live. Soon she found a nice one—in Billy's new shoes.

The next day Billy led the singing in school. Molly Squeak sang, too.

"Squeak, squeak, squeak, squeak."

Billy was pleased to have Molly with him, but his teacher did not care for her.

When school was over, his teacher said, "Billy, please ask your father to get the squeak out of your shoe."

That evening Billy told his father.

"I'll fix Miss Molly," said Father.

He took his hammer and drove a nail into Billy's shoe, scaring poor Molly so much that she hurried out.

Miss Molly Squeak finally found a hiding place in the kitchen door. When anyone opened the door, she sang out loudly and happily.

"Squeak, squeak, squeak, squeak."

But Billy's mother did not care for Molly's singing. After a few days she said, "That squeaking door bothers me. It must be fixed."

Father put something in the places where a squeak could hide. So Molly went sliding out of the kitchen door in a hurry.

Out went Molly into the back yard, wondering where to live next. Father's car stood in the driveway, and Molly looked it over. She found a tiny empty place that was just right. In she went.

The next time Father drove the car, Molly sang, "Squeak, squeak, squeak."

But Father did not care for Molly.

"I'd better have this car fixed and get rid of that awful squeak," he said.

When Molly heard that, she decided to move again. But where?

She had been pushed out of her home in the rocking chair.

She had been hammered out of her home in Billy's shoe.

She had been run out of her home in the kitchen door.

Now she was going to lose her home in the car.

Four homes! And the only place she had really enjoyed was the rocking chair. She went into the house to look for it.

Grandmother Page was sitting in the old rocker, trying to put Janey to sleep. Billy was leaning against the chair back and rocking, too.

Janey's blue eyes were wide open.

"She misses Molly Squeak, and so do I," said Grandmother Page. "This chair hasn't seemed the same since Molly left it."

That was all Molly wanted to hear.

Molly flew closer to the rocker. It had been warm and dry for a long time. The place where the pieces of wood were joined together was loose and empty.

Her old home was ready for her! She rushed into it and began to sing.

"Listen! Miss Molly Squeak has come back!" cried Grandmother, smiling.

Janey listened and then closed her eyes. In a moment she was fast asleep.

Miss Molly was so happy that she sang louder than ever as the chair rocked back and forth.

"Squeak, squeak, squeak."

Animals in Town
and Country

Lady and the Black Dog

It was a warm summer night, and Lady was in her own little house in the back yard.

Just that day the puppy had come to live with Nick Parks. After supper Nick had put her in her little house and told her to lie down and sleep.

But Lady did not lie down and go to sleep. She was unhappy because she was all alone.

She began to cry, making sad little sounds. She hoped that someone would come out of the big house where the Parks family lived. But nobody came.

At last the puppy trotted out of her house and looked around.

The big, round moon was high in the sky. It made the back yard almost as light as day.

There were strange shadows and strange sounds and strange smells in the back yard. Lady wanted to find out about them. So she trotted across the yard in the bright moonlight.

All of a sudden she gave an excited bark. She saw a small black dog crossing the yard just ahead of her.

"Arf, arf, arf," barked Lady with a friendly wag of her tail. Here was a playmate for her.

Quick as a wink Lady jumped at the small black dog. And quick as a wink the other dog jumped away.

"Arf, arf, arf," barked Lady. She was very happy to have a playmate.

"Lady, behave yourself!" Nick called from the porch. "Be quiet!"

"Arf, arf," barked Lady.

Then Nick spoke to the puppy again. "Go and lie down, Lady," he called. "Lie down and go to sleep!"

So Lady turned around to go back to her little house. Now she could not see the black dog, and she was very puzzled. She did not understand how she could have lost her playmate in the bright moonlight.

For a while she ran around sniffing, and then she began barking again.

"Be quiet, Lady!" Nick called from the porch. "Go and lie down."

Lady turned toward the porch, and again she saw the black dog. It had been behind her all the time.

Quick as a wink she scampered after the black dog. And just as quickly the other dog scampered away.

Lady leaped at the black dog again, but still she could not reach it. That puzzled Lady. It was more than she could understand.

Then she began to growl at the other dog and chase it. She chased it all over the yard, but she could not touch it.

Nick ran into the yard to get Lady.

"Poor puppy!" he said. "I suppose you don't like to be alone. I'll take you into the house and let you lie on the floor beside my bed. Maybe that will keep you quiet."

Just then Lady hit at the black dog with one of her little paws. She barked, and she growled.

Nick saw what Lady was chasing, and he began to laugh. Now he could understand why she had been barking and growling.

As he picked up his little dog, he said, "Look at the bright moon, Lady. It fooled you. You have made the funniest mistake a puppy ever made. You thought you were chasing another dog. But instead you were chasing your shadow in the moonlight. Just your own black shadow!"

Fluffytail and the Peanut Hunt

A Joke on Nick

Fluffytail was a squirrel that lived in Grandmother Parks' big front yard.

One morning he looked down from the limb of an oak tree and chattered and chattered. He was excited because he saw Nick Parks hiding peanuts.

Fluffytail wanted those peanuts! But he did not dare go down because Nick's dog was there. It would chase him.

The excited squirrel watched as Nick hid peanuts here and there. He hid some under the dry leaves on the ground. He hid a few behind a stone near the porch. He hid ten or eleven piles of peanuts underneath bushes and behind some vines.

"Ch-ch!" scolded Fluffytail. "Ch-ch!" He wanted those peanuts for himself.

Nick did not look up. He was busy hiding peanuts for his sister Ellen's party.

It was Ellen's fifth birthday, and her grandmother was giving a party to surprise her. All her playmates were going to be guests at the party.

One of the games was to be a peanut hunt. That was why Nick was hiding peanuts in the yard.

When Nick had finished, he put on his roller skates and went skating down the street. Right behind him scampered his frisky little dog.

Now there was no mischievous dog
to chase Fluffytail. Down the tree he
scampered to hunt for peanuts.

He found one peanut under a dry leaf.
Holding it tight in his paws, he sat up
and ate it. Then he looked for more.

He found eleven peanuts behind the
big stone near the porch. He also found
several piles of nuts among the bushes.

Soon little Fluffytail had eaten all he
could hold. Then he began to dig holes
and hide peanuts in the ground. He
kept hiding them, one by one, until he
had taken all he could find.

At two o'clock Grandmother's large, shady yard was full of Ellen's playmates.

Soon Nick and Ellen came and joined the crowd. Ellen was surprised when she saw all the guests and heard them call out, "Happy birthday, Ellen!"

Before Ellen could say anything, her grandmother called to the children. Then she handed each child a paper bag.

"This is for the peanut hunt," she said. "There is a prize for the one who finds the most peanuts."

"Oh!" cried Lily. "I hope I find lots of peanuts."

But Lily did not find lots of peanuts. Nobody else did either.

Lily found eight peanuts under a bush and another one under a dry leaf. Ellen found eleven among the bushes, and Jay found several more behind a vine. The others did not find a single peanut.

"I can't understand that," cried Nick.
"You ought to find dozens of peanuts. I
know where there are several."

He ran to the big stone, while Jay
and Patty followed close behind.

But much to Nick's surprise, there was
not a single peanut behind the stone.
He looked in several other places, but
he could not find any peanuts.

"Somebody took them," Lily said.

That very moment Nick heard a loud
"Ch-ch, ch-ch" from the tree.

"Now I understand what happened," said
Nick. "Somebody did take the peanuts,
and here he is."

A Joke on Fluffytail

"Fluffytail spoiled our peanut hunt," laughed Nick. "He played a joke on me. So I ought to play one on him. I'm going to do it, too."

"How can you?" asked Patty.

"That's a secret," answered Nick. Then he went over and whispered his idea in Grandmother's ear.

While Grandmother took all the guests into the house to play, Nick ran out of the gate. Down the street he dashed, toward a store that sold peanuts.

Then Fluffytail had Grandmother's big yard all to himself. He began to scamper around among the bushes.

But soon he saw Lady coming back with Nick. He knew the dog would chase him. So he did not dare stay on the ground. Up the oak tree the squirrel scampered, as quick as a wink.

Looking down from a limb of the oak tree, Fluffytail saw Nick hiding peanuts again. He was scattering them among the leaves and flowers and bushes.

"Ch-ch!" chattered Fluffytail. More peanuts! This was too good to be true!

Very slowly Fluffytail began to come down the tree. He had almost reached the ground when Lady dashed over to the tree. "Bow-wow! Bow-wow-wow!" she said.

Fluffytail did not dare go a step farther. This time he could not get a single peanut. Lady would not let him. Now the joke was on Fluffytail.

Fluffytail's Prize

When the peanut bag was empty, Nick rang a bell. Then all the guests ran out into the yard for another peanut hunt.

This time they enjoyed the game. They found peanuts among the bushes and leaves, and in all sorts of other places.

Fluffytail looked down from the tree scolding and chattering. He did not like to see somebody else getting all those peanuts.

But Lady was watching him, and he did not dare go down.

The hunt lasted for twenty minutes.
Then Nick rang a bell and the guests
counted their peanuts. Lily had the most
of all. She had found one hundred and
twenty-nine.

Grandmother gave her a storybook.

"Oh, what a nice prize!" said Lily.
"But Fluffytail ought to get a prize, too.
He found more peanuts than any of us.
I know the kind of prize he'd like."

Lily went skipping around scattering
peanuts from her bag. But Fluffytail did
not get his prize until the dog and the
children had gone. Then he had another
peanut hunt all by himself.

Chip, the Baby Chipmunk

Nick Feeds Chip

Sniff, sniff, sniff went Chip, the baby chipmunk. He had come out from his home underneath a big log because he smelled food. Somebody was cooking breakfast among the trees nearby.

Chip wanted some of that breakfast himself, but his mother had taught him to be careful. She had taught him to keep away from people.

So Chip did not go any farther. He just watched the Parks family.

They had come to the big forest that Monday. Already they had done many sorts of things that Chip could not understand. They had put up a tent and laid bags and boxes on the ground.

Now Mrs. Parks was baking corn-meal pancakes at the big stone fireplace.

Chip forgot that his mother had taught him to be careful, and he went closer.

All of a sudden Nick pointed to Chip and shouted, "Look at that chipmunk!"

With one short squeak, the little fellow dashed into his hole.

"It's too bad I scared him," said Nick. "He'd be a fine pet to take home. I wonder if I can tame him while we're here on our vacation."

"Maybe you can," said Mr. Parks. "Next time you see him, don't move and don't make any noise."

"Perhaps he'd be as easy to tame as Fluffytail," said Nick. "I've just taught the squirrel to eat out of my hand. I think I can teach this chipmunk, too. I'll begin right now."

Nick walked to the log and laid out several bits of corn-meal pancake and a piece of orange.

"I wish he'd come and get it," thought Nick. But Chip did not come.

At last Nick scattered the food on the ground. Chip peeped out at the bits of pancake and the piece of orange.

He never had eaten anything but nuts, weed seeds, and other things he found in the forest. Chip wanted this strange food very much.

But he had been taught to keep away from people. So he did not dare come out of his hole until the boy had gone into the tent.

Then the little chipmunk became brave enough to scamper over to the food.

Chip sat up on his hind legs, held the piece of orange between his tiny paws, and began to eat it. The orange tasted much better than weed seeds.

Then he nibbled the bits of corn-meal pancake that were scattered on the ground. When he had eaten them all, he scampered back into his hole.

That was Monday morning. All day Monday and all day Tuesday Chip kept finding food scattered near the log. There were bits of fruit and other sorts of food from the people's table.

Chip ate everything—even a bit of boiled potato. He was not frightened now. Little by little he was getting tame.

Chip Eats Chocolate Cookies

By Tuesday evening Chip became so brave that he even dared to climb on the table near the tent. There he saw a box of chocolate cookies that somebody had laid on the table.

Chip gnawed a hole in the box with his sharp teeth and began to nibble at the chocolate cookies. He was so busy nibbling that he did not hear Nick coming.

"Oh!" cried Nick. "So you're nibbling at our chocolate cookies! Now I know how to set a trap for you."

Nick's voice scared Chip. With a short, frightened squeak the chipmunk rushed straight home.

But the next morning Chip felt brave again. Back he came and found the same box of chocolate cookies.

If he had stopped to look, he would have seen a bigger wooden box above it. The wooden box was held up by a stick that had a string fastened to it.

This was the trap that Nick had set. If the stick was pulled out, the wooden box would fall over the cookie box.

The chipmunk did not see that Nick was nearby, ready to pull the string. He did not know there was any danger. So he went right up to the cookie box.

Before he could take a single nibble, Nick pulled the string. Crash! The stick fell. Then down crashed the big box. Chip was caught in Nick's trap.

Ellen heard the crash and ran out of the tent to look at the chipmunk.

With frightened squeaks he dashed back and forth in the wooden box.

"Nick," begged Ellen, "please let the chipmunk go. He'd like to be free."

"Oh, no!" answered Nick. "He'll soon be tame, and we'll have a fine pet to take home from our vacation."

So Nick kept Chip in the box all day.

At nine o'clock that evening, everything was quiet. Nobody was stirring about when Mother Chipmunk climbed on the table and joined her baby. She began to gnaw the box with her sharp teeth.

Inside the box Chip's sharp teeth were gnawing. Both chipmunks gnawed and gnawed. But gnawing that wooden box was slow work.

The noise woke Nick, who was asleep in the tent. In the moonlight he could see brave Mother Chipmunk gnawing at the box to set her baby free. When she heard somebody stirring, she dashed off.

But Chip kept gnawing at the box.

"I hate to give him up," thought Nick. "He'd be a fine pet, but he wants to be free. I probably ought to let him go."

Stepping outside, Nick lifted the box. Quick as a wink Chip dashed away. In a few seconds he was safe in his home.

Salt for the Deer

Watching the Deer

Early one morning Mother Deer led her two babies quietly through the green forest until they came to a wide, sunny meadow. Here they stood very still.

Then Mother Deer left the two babies in the shadows among the trees and stepped out alone into the sunlight.

Mother Deer had sharp eyes and sharp ears. She looked all around and listened carefully. She wanted to see if there were any signs of danger before going any farther.

But she could not see or hear or smell any fierce wild animals that might hurt her babies. So she crossed the meadow to a pool of water and began to drink.

The fawns never stirred from their place in the shadows until their mother wagged her tail. That was a signal for them to follow her. Then they pranced across the meadow and went to the pool.

While the fawns were drinking, their mother raised her head. Again she listened for any signs of danger.

For a while the only sounds near the pool were bird calls. The tweet-tweet of a robin, the screaming of a bluejay, and the cawing of a crow filled the air.

Suddenly there was a loud sneeze. The Parks family had been watching the doe and her two fawns.

The moment Mother Deer heard the sneeze, she signaled to the fawns and dashed into the forest. The fawns were close behind her. In a few seconds all three deer were out of sight.

"Oh," said Nick, "it's too bad I sneezed and frightened the deer."

"You couldn't help sneezing," said Mrs. Parks. "Anyway, the deer probably will come back tomorrow."

"Will they?" said Nick. "Well, if the deer come here every day to drink, I might be able to tame the two fawns. I could have them for pets."

"Now, Nick," laughed his father, "just remember Chip. Do you want to trap the fawns?"

"No," said Nick. "I know that would be a foolish thing to do. Chip taught me a lesson. I want the fawns to be free, but I'd like to tame them while we're on vacation."

"Why don't you put salt on their tails," laughed Ellen. "I've heard of catching birds that way."

"That's not such a joke as you seem to think," said Father. "Probably we can tame the fawns with salt. All deer love salt. The storekeeper in town has some blocks of salt. I'll buy a block on Monday when I go to town."

Taming the Deer

On Monday afternoon Mr. Parks bought a block of salt. Monday evening he set it out in the meadow for the deer.

The doe and her two babies visited the meadow early on Tuesday morning. Mother Deer noticed the big block of salt right away. She went over and sniffed at it while the fawns waited in the shadows.

The Parks family were hiding among the bushes. They enjoyed watching the beautiful animals. But Nick forgot that he ought to be quiet and began to speak.

That spoiled everything. Quick as a wink the doe leaped away from the salt block. Off she dashed with her babies close behind her.

Nick waited all Tuesday morning to see if the deer would come back, but he did not see them again that day.

Next morning the three deer visited the meadow again. This time the doe had signaled her fawns to join her at the salt block.

Nick was watching from the bushes. He did not stir, and Mother Deer did not notice that anybody was there.

The doe and her fawns stayed about twenty minutes, licking the salt block with their pink tongues.

Then Nick had an idea. He decided that each night he would move the block of salt a little nearer to the tent.

Every night for the rest of the week Nick moved the block of salt a little bit nearer to the tent. And the deer did not seem to mind. Each morning they came nearer to Nick. Soon he could see their pink tongues go in and out as they licked the salt.

"The deer are getting tame already," said Nick. "They're not afraid to come near the tent. Next week is the end of our vacation. Probably I can still tame them if I hurry up. On Monday I'll let them see me."

So on Monday Nick did not hide. When the three deer crossed the meadow, he was sitting on the ground near the block of salt. He sat as still as a stone.

To Nick's great joy, the doe and her fawns did not run away. But they would not come close to Nick. They just stood still and looked at him and at the salt.

Nick was in sight again on Tuesday when the deer came to the meadow. He sat just as near the block of salt as he had on Monday.

The doe looked at him with her big eyes. Slowly she went over to the block of salt and began to lick it.

She watched Nick. When he did not stir, she wagged her tail as a signal to the fawns. They came prancing across the meadow and joined her.

One fawn began to nibble at the grass, while the other one sniffed at Nick's leg.

Nick wanted to shout with joy, but he did not move or make a sound. He hardly dared to take a breath.

"The deer are almost tame now!" he thought. "Tomorrow I'll hold some salt in my hand and see what they'll do. Probably they'll run away, but I'd like to try it before our vacation is over."

The next morning Nick held a piece of
salt and waited without stirring.

Soon the doe and her fawns came out
of the shadows and crossed the meadow.

To Nick's joy, one fawn put out its
tongue and licked the salt in his hand.
Finally the other fawn licked it, too.

"They are both tame," thought Nick.
"They're tame, and yet they're free!"

When the deer had gone, Ellen ran
out from behind a bush.

"You did tame the fawns with salt!"
cried Ellen. "Only you put the salt on
their tongues instead of on their tails!"

The Bears' Picnic

With a push of her big, strong paw Mother Bear turned a log over and uncovered hundreds of bugs. She and her two little cubs began to gobble the bugs as fast as they could.

A wren and a woodpecker flew down. They wanted to eat some bugs, too, but they did not have a chance to get any.

In a minute the bears had eaten all those hundreds of bugs. Mother Bear gave a low grunt and waddled off. The cubs followed her.

Soon Mother Bear noticed some bushes that were full of berries. She began to gobble the juicy berries as fast as she could. The cubs watched her for a moment. Then they began to eat the juicy berries, too.

When the berries were gone, Mother Bear stood up on her hind legs and began to sniff.

The cubs also stood up and began to sniff. There were wonderful, wonderful smells in the air.

With a grunt Mother Bear started off, and the cubs followed her.

Soon they saw something that made their mouths water. A picnic lunch was spread out. There were plates of fruit and sandwiches and four cups of milk.

The Parks family were just sitting down to lunch. Their vacation was over, and they were on their way home. They had to be there by Monday.

Nick sat down and picked up a plate. "I'm as hungry as a bear," he said.

Just then Mr. Parks looked up and saw the three bears coming toward them.

"Jump in the car! Quick!" he cried.

The family got in the automobile and watched the bears through the windows.

The cubs knocked over the paper cups. They grabbed sandwiches and hard-boiled eggs and fruit from the paper plates and gobbled them up.

Then Mother Bear saw some cup cakes all covered with thick white frosting. She grabbed two of the cup cakes and tried to eat both of them at once.

This was the first chance she had ever had to eat cake, and how she enjoyed it! Mother Bear got frosting on her paws, frosting on her mouth, and frosting on her neck. It stuck to her fur and made her look very funny.

"How would you like to tame those mischievous bears, Nick?" laughed Ellen.

"Well," said Nick, "if we were just starting on our vacation, I might try."

One cub found a tall can of chocolate cookies. He put his head in and ate and ate until the can was empty.

When he had finished all the cookies, he tried to pull his head out. But it was stuck tight in the empty can.

He raised and twisted his head, but the cookie can would not come off.

Finally when Mother Bear had licked the frosting from her paws, she waddled over to her cub. Bang, bang! She hit the tin can twice, and away it flew.

"Bears are the funniest animals in the world!" laughed Nick.

Then one cub licked some frosting from a plate. In and out went his pink tongue as he licked the plate clean.

The other cub grabbed a glass of jam and licked it clean.

Those mischievous bears ate everything. They ate sandwiches, cookies, six juicy oranges, and some other fruit. They ate a dozen hard-boiled eggs, shells and all. They ate ten cup cakes with thick frosting. And when the bears ran off, Mother Bear had spots of frosting in her fur.

The Parks family laughed and laughed.

"This has been a wonderful end to our vacation," said Nick.

"Yes," said Mother, "but now we have no lunch. The bears ate everything but the cups and plates and the jam glass."

Nick said, "That's all right. I thought I was as hungry as a bear. But I'm not as hungry as those bears were."

Ringtail, the Young Raccoon

Ringtail Sees the World

Ringtail wanted to go down the big tree, down to the ground below.

He was a young raccoon with thick, dark fur and a fine bushy tail. Ringtail lived with his family in a hole in the trunk of the tree.

Little Sister was now fast asleep in the hole. She would go on sleeping until Mother and Father Raccoon came home with food.

226

Tonight was Ringtail's chance to go and see the strange world below.

So the furry little fellow started down the tree. Nobody had ever taught him to climb down a tree, but he knew just what to do.

He had to hold tight to the bark of the tree with his sharp nails. Slowly and carefully he moved along. Down, down he went toward the ground below. It seemed a long way down, but finally he reached the bottom.

Peeping through the tall weeds and bushes, Ringtail started bravely off to see the world.

Suddenly the air was filled with sound. There were the fierce squawks of a bird, the croaking of frogs, and the swishing of branches.

Now the little raccoon was beginning to be afraid. But he went on until he heard a loud crash of thunder. Twice more he heard the thunder crash.

Ringtail did not feel very brave now. He did not go one step farther. Back to his tree and up the trunk he dashed, twice as fast as he had come down.

Ringtail popped into his hole just as the thunder crashed again.

The little raccoon did not stir out of his home again that night. He did not want to see any more of the strange world just then.

Ringtail Goes Fishing

One evening several weeks later, the two young raccoons were taken on a fishing trip by their father and mother.

Just as the big, round moon began to shine, the raccoons started for the river.

Stepping carefully, Father Raccoon led his family through the thick forest. The moonlight made queer-looking shadows on the ground, and the night air was full of strange sounds.

But this time Ringtail was not afraid. Little Sister was not afraid either. The two young raccoons were sure that their mother and father would take good care of them.

They traveled along until they reached the river bank. Then Father Raccoon gave his children a fishing lesson. He walked into the water and felt around on the sandy bottom with his paws.

Soon he came back with something in his mouth. It looked like a round stone, but it was a clam shell.

Father Raccoon had seen shells like that before. He knew that if he pulled the shell apart, he would find a juicy clam inside. Sure enough, when he pulled the shell apart, there was a nice, juicy clam!

Little Sister tried to grab the clam, but Father Raccoon kept it and swished it around in the water. He was showing how to wash the clam.

When Father Raccoon had taught Little Sister how to wash the clam, he gave it to her. The furry baby grabbed it and popped it into her mouth.

Then Mother Raccoon found a clam and pulled the shell apart. Ringtail quickly grabbed that clam, washed it, and popped it into his mouth.

After he had eaten several big, juicy clams, Ringtail wanted to catch one all by himself.

He walked bravely into the stream and began to feel around on the sandy bottom for clam shells. Ringtail was in a great hurry. He moved his paws over the bottom of the stream as fast as he could.

All at once Ringtail cried out. One of his paws was caught. He had put it inside a clam shell that was open. Quickly the shell had closed up tight! The clam had caught Ringtail!

The poor little fellow twisted and turned his paw, but he could not get it free. The shell would not come apart.

With a loud cry Ringtail started for the bank of the stream.

Little Sister and the two grown-up raccoons came running to see what was the matter.

Ringtail hopped out of the stream on three legs and held up the paw with the clam shell on it.

Father Raccoon took hold of the shell and began to pull it apart. In just a moment he had it open.

Then the little raccoon lay down on the bank of the stream and licked his paw. It hurt, but after he had licked it a while, it began to feel better.

Little Sister caught some clams. She pulled the shells apart and washed the clams. Then she popped the juicy food into her mouth.

Soon Ringtail was back in the stream bravely catching clams, too. This time he did not make the mistake of moving his paws too fast. Now he was smart. He caught several juicy clams without being caught himself.

Paddle Tail

Paddle Tail and his twin sister, Water Baby, swam out of the doorway of their house in the big pond. They were right behind Mother Beaver, and they followed her to the top of the pool of water.

The beaver twins splashed and swam and swam and splashed in their pond. They swam down into the water and slowly up to the smooth, glassy top again.

The water was cold, and the sun felt warm and pleasant on the beavers' wet, furry backs.

All at once there was a noise among the trees, and some people came out of the woods.

Mother Beaver was frightened. She raised her thick, flat tail and brought it down on the water with a hard slap.

When the beaver twins heard the slap, they dived straight down into the pond and hid in their house.

Then Mother Beaver dived down and hid there with them.

That slapping noise was her danger signal. No beaver makes such a noise unless danger is very near.

For a while the three beavers stayed in their house and hid. But finally Mother Beaver swam back toward the top of the water. Close behind her swam the twins.

One by one the three brown heads bobbed up to the top of the pool.

Soon Mother Beaver swam over to the shore of the pond and called to the twins. After they joined her, she led them away from the pool and into the forest.

All of a sudden she smelled a wolf. Quickly she pushed the little beavers into the shadows behind a thick, bushy vine. They stayed there without stirring.

Just then a fawn dashed past them. Close behind it came a fierce gray wolf.

The fawn made a quick turn and got away. But the wolf was going so fast that he kept straight on. He did not notice the beavers.

Mother Beaver and her twins were safe, but they were shaking with fright.

The three beavers waited quietly for several minutes. Then they left the pool and hurried into the green forest.

Soon they came to the shore of a large pond where there were several beaver houses. Some young beavers were playing on a log not far from shore.

Paddle Tail and his sister watched the strangers dive into the deep pool. One by one the smooth wet heads bobbed up as the strangers swam to the top again.

Paddle Tail could hardly wait for a chance to join these strangers. His twin had been his only playmate because no other beaver families lived in their family's pool.

When Mother Beaver dived into the water, both furry babies followed her.

All three swam straight to the log where the strangers were playing and climbed up on it. Then they, too, began diving into the pond and bobbing up again.

For a while it was fun to splash and dive in the pond with playmates. But all of a sudden Paddle Tail stopped his play and became quiet. He had noticed something moving among the trees on the shore.

Looking closely, Paddle Tail saw the gray fur of a wolf. The fierce animal was not far away from some big beavers that were resting on the shore.

Slap! In his fright the little beaver brought his flat tail down on the water as hard as he could. That was a danger signal. Unless those big beavers dived into the water, the wolf would get them.

After Paddle Tail had given the danger signal, he dived into the pond quick as a wink.

The other beavers dived, too.

Out of sight went Paddle Tail's mother and sister and all their playmates. The big beavers on shore also dived, and just in time.

It was lucky that Paddle Tail had noticed the wolf and given the danger signal. The big, fierce animal had been very close to the beavers on the shore.

For a while the beavers did not come back to the top of the water. But finally they all got over their fright. One by one their smooth brown heads came bobbing up to the top of the pond.

They looked about them carefully, but their enemy had gone.

Paddle Tail and Water Baby bobbed up, too, and joined their playmates on the log. They all dived into the cool pond and bobbed up to the top again. Down and up, down and up!

With great joy the twins splashed there with their new playmates for the rest of the summer.

Chuckle Makes a Friend

One summer day Chuckle lay in the sunshine on a stone wall. He was a fat, furry young ground hog that loved to lie in the sun.

Nearby, Chuckle's mother was nibbling at an ear of corn. Suddenly she dropped it and gave a loud whistle.

Chuckle knew that the whistle was a signal. His mother never whistled that way unless danger was near.

Chuckle knew he should run home, but he wanted to see what the danger was.

He did not have to wait long. In a moment he saw a large dog. The little ground hog jumped up in fright. Into his hole under the stone wall he popped.

His mother also dashed for the hole. Already the big dog was so close that his sharp teeth almost caught her tail.

With an angry growl, the dog poked his nose between the rocks in the wall. He poked and growled, but he could not reach the ground hogs.

Chuckle never forgot the fright the dog had given him. When he grew old enough to have a home of his own, he made a deep hole under a tree. There he would be safe from dogs. He knew that they were his enemies and would hurt him if they could.

He made his home between a clover field and a stream. In the clover field he could get food. In the stream he could get plenty of water.

One morning when Chuckle was asleep in his hole, a clap of thunder woke him. The thunder roared and rain poured down, but the ground hog went back to sleep.

All day the thunderstorm kept up, and late in the afternoon water began to pour into Chuckle's home. Then he woke up and rushed to his doorway to see what was the matter.

It had rained so much that there was a big flood. Already the stream had spread over the clover field, and still the storm kept on.

Chuckle knew he would not be safe unless he found a place above the water.

Finally Chuckle saw a steep rock in the middle of the clover field. He probably could reach that rock. And if he got there, he would be safe from the flood.

Chuckle did not want to go through the storm and the flood. But he had to get to that rock.

Off he splashed, with the thunder crashing and the rain pouring down. When he could walk no longer through the water, he swam.

Chuckle finally reached the high rock. His thick brown fur was wet and muddy. He was so tired that he could hardly climb up the rock. Twice he went sliding down its steep sides and fell back into the cold water.

But at last he reached the top. Then he stopped in fright. There on the rock was one of his hated enemies—a dog!

Chuckle looked closer and saw that the dog was a puppy about his own size. The puppy did not look like an enemy. But Chuckle was going to stay on that rock even if he had to fight.

The puppy did not fight or even growl. He hardly bothered to look at Chuckle.

The puppy and Chuckle stayed on the rock as far apart as they could. All during the stormy night they lay there while the flood grew worse and worse.

By morning the water was so deep that only the very top of the steep rock was uncovered. Chuckle and the puppy did not lie far apart like enemies now. They lay side by side.

In the morning it stopped raining. Before noon the sun began to shine over the flooded clover field.

But the water did not go down very fast even after the storm was over. So Chuckle and the puppy stayed on the rock all that day and all that night. During the night they drew closer and closer together to keep warm.

By the next morning the flood had gone down. The puppy jumped off the rock and trotted through the mud to his home. Then Chuckle walked away to see if his home was dry.

Nearly a year had passed, and spring had come. Chuckle was walking in the clover field one day when he came to a steep rock. It was the same rock where he had stayed during the flood. He climbed to the top to enjoy the warm spring sun.

Suddenly a dog twice Chuckle's size jumped on the rock. He growled fiercely as if he wanted to fight. Chuckle stood up, ready to fight an enemy. But the big dog stopped growling and began to sniff. Instead of fighting, he wagged his tail with joy.

Chuckle sniffed, too. Then he knew it was the puppy he had met during the flood. He had grown to be a big dog now—twice the size of Chuckle. But he still was not an enemy.

The two friends lay down on the big rock and enjoyed the warm sun during the whole afternoon.

On the Roads
of Long Ago

The Lad and the North Wind

The Magic Cloth

Long ago and far away a poor lad lived with his mother near an old, old village.

One cold winter day the mother was going to make porridge. But first the lad had to go to the village for meal.

As he returned with the meal, along came the North Wind puffing and blowing. The Wind puffed at the meal with his strong breath and scattered it in the air.

The lad became very angry.

"I'll travel to the North Wind's home and get that meal," he said. "I'll make the Wind give it back to me."

The weather was cold and the way
was long, but at last the lad reached
the North Wind's home.

"GOOD DAY!" roared the North Wind
in a gruff voice. "What do you want?"

"I want you to give back our meal,"
said the lad. "We need it for porridge."

"I can't give back your meal," said
the North Wind. "I don't have it. But
I'll give you this tablecloth instead. It's
a good cloth. It's worth more than all
the meal in the world.

"When you are hungry, you must say,
'Cloth, cloth, spread yourself.' Then it
will serve you all sorts of good food."

The lad thanked the North Wind, put the cloth under his jacket, and started for his home.

It grew dark early that winter day. So he stopped at an inn for the night.

After resting for a while, the lad laid the cloth on a table and said, "Cloth, cloth, spread yourself."

At once the cloth served dinner. It served hot bread with honey and cheese. It served a roast duck and two roast geese.

When the man who kept the inn saw this, he thought, "That magic tablecloth would be worth a lot to me."

The innkeeper was a wicked man. He decided to steal the magic cloth when he had a chance. As soon as his guests were asleep, he took the magic cloth and laid another cloth beside the lad's bed.

In the morning the lad put the cloth under his jacket and went home.

"Look," he said to his mother, pulling out the cloth. "I have traveled to the North Wind's home, and he has given me a magic cloth. This is worth more than all the meal in the world. It's a real treasure.

"When I want food, it serves me hot bread with honey and cheese. It also serves me roast ducks and roast geese."

"I'll never believe that unless I see it," said his mother.

So the boy laid the cloth on a table and said, "Cloth, cloth, spread yourself." But the cloth did not serve a bit of food.

The Magic Sheep

The lad returned to the North Wind. "Good day, North Wind!" he called.

"GOOD DAY," roared the North Wind in his gruff voice. "What is it you want now?"

"I want my meal," said the lad. "That cloth you gave me isn't worth a penny. It won't serve me even a piece of cheese or a bit of dry bread."

"I can't give back your meal," said the North Wind. "I don't have it. But I'll give you this magic sheep instead. It's a very good sheep. It is worth more than all the meal in the world.

"Whenever you need money, just say, 'Sheep, sheep, give money.' Then the sheep will open its mouth, and golden coins will drop out."

The lad thanked the North Wind and went off, leading the sheep by a rope.

That evening the lad went to the inn, leading his sheep. After he had eaten his supper, he said, "Sheep, sheep, give money."

At once the sheep's mouth opened, and golden coins dropped out.

"Golden coins!" cried the other guests. "What a wonderful sheep!"

"Oho!" thought the wicked innkeeper. "That sheep would be worth a lot to me. I'll steal it tonight. Then I'll have thousands of golden coins and be rich."

When everyone was asleep, the wicked
innkeeper had a chance to steal the magic
sheep. In its place he left another sheep.

The next morning the lad went home,
leading his sheep behind him.

"Mother," cried the lad, "look at this
sheep the North Wind has given me. It
is a real treasure. It is worth more
than all the meal in the world. It gives
me golden coins when I ask for them."

"I'll never believe that unless I see
it," said his mother.

So the lad said, "Sheep, sheep, give
money!" But it did not give one coin.

The Magic Stick

The lad returned to the North Wind and said, "I want my meal. That sheep you gave me isn't worth a penny."

"I can't give back your meal," roared the North Wind. "But I'll give you this magic stick instead.

"It's very useful. If you ever want it to beat somebody, just say, 'Beat, stick, beat.' It will keep on beating until you say, 'Stick, stop beating.' "

"Oho!" said the lad. "I shall find it useful." By this time he had guessed that the wicked innkeeper had taken his magic cloth and his magic sheep.

That night the lad returned to the inn. When the innkeeper saw the stick, he felt sure it was a magic one. After the guests were asleep, he crept to the lad's bed. He laid another stick beside the lad and snatched the magic stick.

The lad was only pretending to sleep. Quickly he cried, "Beat, stick, beat!"

It began to beat the man at once. It beat him until he screamed, "Don't! Don't hit me! Don't hit me!"

He ran wildly this way and that. He crashed over tables and chairs, but the stick followed and kept on beating him.

"Save me! Save me!" he called to the lad. "Make your stick stop beating me! I'll give back your magic cloth and your sheep. This will be a lesson to me. I'll never steal anything again."

"Stick, stop beating," called the lad, and the stick dropped to the floor.

When the innkeeper had given back the magic cloth and the magic sheep, the lad was happy.

"The North Wind is a good fellow after all," he thought. "These are very useful gifts he has given me. These gifts are worth a thousand times as much as the meal that the North Wind blew away. They are real treasures."

When morning came, the happy lad woke up and put on his hat and jacket. He went home with the North Wind's gifts, and he never was poor again.

The Fairy Shoemaker

Tom Looks for a Pot of Gold

Once there was a boy named Tom who was always wishing to be rich. One day he said to his mother, "I'll find the Fairy Shoemaker. He knows where there is a huge pot filled with thousands of gold coins. I'll make him tell his secret."

Tom's mother smiled and said, "The Fairy Shoemaker is a sly elf. I think you'll become rich sooner if you do some useful work and earn your golden coins."

But Tom did not like to work, and he started out to hunt for the elf.

Every day that week Tom hunted for the Fairy Shoemaker in the woods and in the meadows.

At last one afternoon Tom heard a tiny tapping sound behind a tree.

Tick-a-tack, tick-a-tack,
Tick-a-tack-too.

At first it seemed to be the tapping of a woodpecker. But when Tom listened closely, he could hear somebody singing softly in a tiny voice,

"Tick-a-tack, tick-a-tack,
Tick-a-tack-too.
Tack a toe, tack a heel.
Soon we'll have a shoe."

Tom crept quietly toward the voice.

"Oho!" he thought. "That must be the song of the Fairy Shoemaker. I'll catch him, and then he'll have to lead me to the huge pot of gold. Soon my mother and I will be rich."

Tom crept forward on his hands and
knees until he saw the Fairy Shoemaker.
The tiny elf had a long nose and a
pointed chin. He wore a tall cap and
an apron.

The elf was busy pounding tacks into
a tiny shoe that was upside down in
front of him. As he worked, he sang,

> "Tick-a-tack, tick-a-tack,
>
> Tick-a-tack-too.
>
> Tack a toe, tack a heel.
>
> Soon we'll have a shoe."

"Good day," said Tom politely. But
the elf pretended not to hear. He did
not even glance at Tom.

"Show me the pot of gold," cried Tom.

"Wait a minute," said the elf. "I have just dropped a tack. Help me find it."

Tom knew that if he took his eyes off the Fairy Shoemaker for a second, the sly little elf would disappear.

"I'll just pretend to look for the tack," thought Tom. Slowly he crept forward on his hands and knees. But the sly elf snatched up some dust and threw it in Tom's face.

The dust made Tom sneeze. When he sneezed, he shut his eyes. He opened them quickly, but the elf had disappeared.

Tom Tries Again

Tom was not ready to give up. He said to himself, "If I found the Fairy Shoemaker once, I can find him twice. Next time I won't let him throw dust in my face and make me sneeze."

Every day Tom hunted for the sly elf. On the fifth day he heard the tap, tap, tap of the Fairy Shoemaker's hammer again. He listened closely, and soon he heard the elf singing,

"Tick-a-tack, tick-a-tack,
Tick-a-tack-too.
Tack a toe, tack a heel.
Soon we'll have a shoe."

Tom crept forward until he could see the elf sitting in the shade of a tree.

"Now," thought Tom, "I won't let him throw dust in my face. And I'll keep my eyes on him so that he can't disappear. I won't glance away once."

The Fairy Shoemaker was pounding tacks into the toe of a tiny shoe that was upside down in front of him.

"That's a fine shoe," said Tom as he crept slowly forward.

He kept his eyes on the elf every minute so that the little man would not disappear.

"Why are you working?" asked Tom.

"We should all work," answered the elf without glancing up. "You ought to do a little work yourself."

"Ho, ho, ho!" laughed Tom. "That would be foolish. I don't need to work. I'll become rich without working."

Quick as a wink Tom rose from his knees and grabbed the Fairy Shoemaker.

"I have caught you at last," cried Tom. "Now you can't throw dust in my face and make me sneeze. And I won't let you go unless you lead me to the huge pot of gold."

"Well," said the elf, "if I must show you my treasure, I suppose I must."

Off they went into the thick woods.

"You will find the huge pot of gold there," said the elf, pointing to the foot of a tree. "Dig there for the treasure."

"I'll have to go home for a shovel," said Tom. "But first I'll put my yellow tie around this tree. Then I can find the right tree when I come back."

Tom glanced at the Fairy Shoemaker and saw that he was smiling slyly.

"Will you promise not to touch this tie while I am gone?" asked Tom.

"Yes, I promise not to touch it," said the sly elf. "And I promise not to let anybody else touch it either."

"Then I'll let you go free," said Tom, setting the Fairy Shoemaker down.

"Thanks for leading me to the gold."

"Ho, ho, ho!" laughed the elf. "You'll find that you have to work for any gold you ever get."

Pop! The next second the laughing elf had disappeared.

Tom got a shovel and hurried back to the woods. He could hardly wait to begin digging for the treasure.

"Now I'll be rich!" he cried with joy. "I caught the Fairy Shoemaker, and he told me his secret."

When Tom returned to the woods, he gave a whistle of surprise. Every single tree had a yellow tie around it.

The Fairy Shoemaker had kept his promise. Nobody had touched Tom's tie, but the sly elf had fooled him again.

"I can't tell which tie is mine," said Tom, almost in tears. "Now I'll never be able to find the secret treasure."

Finally Tom turned sadly toward his home. "It's true," he said. "Mother is right. I'll become rich sooner if I do some useful work and earn my gold."

The Turtle's Race

One day a turtle was crawling slowly down a path in a shady woods. Down the same path came a rabbit, kicking up his heels as he hopped along. Just as he passed the turtle, he stopped.

"Good morning, turtle," said the rabbit. "Where are you going?"

"I am on my way to the river," said the turtle as he crawled slowly along.

"Ho, ho! Ho, ho!" laughed the rabbit. "You never will reach the river if you keep crawling along in that slow way. You ought to try hopping for a change. That's the way to get to the river in a hurry."

"I can't hop like you," said the turtle. "I can only crawl. But I'll get to the river just the same. Perhaps I'll get there before you do."

"Ho, ho, ho!" laughed the rabbit. "Do you really think you can beat me? Shall we have a race?"

"I don't mind if we do," answered the turtle. "And maybe I'll win."

As they started off, the turtle crawled slowly along the path. But the rabbit kicked up his heels and hopped so fast that he left the slow turtle far behind.

Before long the rabbit became tired and out of breath. Then he made a foolish mistake. He sat down to rest.

"I am almost at the river," he said. "That slow turtle can't win this race. I think I'll lie down and take a nap."

The rabbit lay down in the shade of a bush. Soon he was fast asleep.

The turtle kept on crawling. It looked as if he did not have a chance to win. The rabbit was so far ahead that he was out of sight.

But the slow turtle did not stop once. He did not get tired or out of breath. Slowly but surely he crawled along the path.

After a while he passed the rabbit, still taking his nap in the shade.

"Oho, what luck!" said the turtle with a little chuckle. "When that foolish rabbit wakes up from his nap, he won't think he's so clever. I'll fool him yet."

After a long nap the rabbit woke up.

"Well, well," he said with a big yawn. "The turtle is not in sight. I might as well go to the river and wait for that slow fellow to come crawling along."

Down to the river he went, kicking up his heels happily. But when the rabbit got there, he was so surprised that he stood right up on his hind legs. There on the bank of the river was the turtle!

"I can't understand how in the world you got here ahead of me," cried the rabbit. "How did you do it?"

"By crawling along slowly but surely," said the turtle. "That's the way to win. I may be slow, but I am sure."

The Golden Pears

The Oldest Son's Trip

Once there was a man who had a pear tree that was the great joy of his life.

One summer day he picked a dozen fine pears and laid the fruit in a basket.

"Take these pears to the king," the man said to his oldest son. "They are the finest pears in the whole world. If the king likes them, he will give you a wonderful present, which you must bring back to me."

The two younger sons wanted to go along and see the huge palace, where even the servants were dressed in velvet.

But the father said, "No, your oldest brother is the one to go. He will know how to get a present from the king."

He turned to his oldest son and said, "Take the shortest road to the palace. And don't let anybody steal the pears."

"Oh, they'll be safe with me," said the lad. "I won't let anybody steal them. I'm too clever for that."

Off he went, whistling happily.

After the oldest son had walked for
several miles, he came to a big field of
clover. There he saw an old woman
taking honey from a beehive.

She had a long nose, sharp eyes, and
a pointed chin. She looked like a witch,
and she was a witch.

"What do you have in your basket,
my lad," she asked in a squeaky voice.

"Just some dirt," said the lad slyly.

"It's dirt, is it?" shouted the witch.
"Well, my lad, you'll pay for your
clever tongue. You'll see if it really is
dirt when your trip is ended."

When the lad reached the palace, the servants took him to the throne room. Soon the king came in and sat on his throne. He wore brightly colored velvet clothes, and he had a crown on his head.

The boy dropped down on one knee. "Oh, King," he said, "I have brought you some pears, the best in the world."

But when the king uncovered the lad's basket, he saw nothing but dirt. The witch had made the boy's words come true. She had changed the pears to dirt.

The king threw down the basket of dirt and roared, "Lock this fellow up. And keep him locked up!"

The Second Son's Trip

For several days the father waited for his oldest son to return. Then he said to his second son, "Take these ripe pears to the king. He will give you golden coins or some other wonderful reward."

On his way to the palace the lad saw the old witch at her beehives.

"What is in your basket?" she asked.

The lad felt sure she wanted to steal his pears. So he said, "Just pig food."

"Pig food!" she shouted. "Well, my lad, you'll pay for your sly, clever tongue! You'll see if it's pig food when your trip is ended."

Sure enough, when the king uncovered the basket, he found pig food. The witch had changed the ripe pears to pig food.

"Lock this fellow up," cried the king. "And keep him locked up!" So the second son was locked up with his brother.

The Youngest Son's Trip

When the second son did not return, the youngest son said, "Father, let me take some ripe pears to the king. If the king gives me a fine reward, I'll bring it back. Then you'll be rich for the rest of your life."

"You're only a young lad," said the father. "How can you win a reward if your clever brothers had no luck?"

But the lad begged and begged, until his father said that he might go and try his luck.

After the lad had walked along for several miles, he came to the clover field. There was the old witch with the long nose and the pointed chin.

"Good day," said the lad pleasantly.

"Good day," said the witch. As she spoke, she thought, "Here at last is a lad with a friendly tongue in his head."

"You are carrying a heavy load," said the witch. "What is in your basket?"

"Ripe pears from my father's tree," answered the boy politely. "They are the finest pears in all the world. They are as yellow as real gold."

"Oho!" said the witch. "So you have ripe, golden pears! Well, you are a friendly lad with a friendly tongue in your head. You'll see what is in your basket when your trip is ended."

After saying good-by to the witch, the boy went on to the palace, whistling happily.

The lad told the King's servants that his father had sent a basket of fine, ripe pears to the king.

"Pears!" shouted one of the servants. "Go away, or we'll lock you up." Then he slapped the poor boy.

Another servant slapped him, too, and kicked him and tried to grab his basket.

Just then the princess came out of the palace. She wore a velvet dress and a beautiful crown of gold. Taking a step forward, she spoke to the lad.

The lad went down on one knee and said, "My father sent these ripe pears to the king. But the servants will not let me into the throne room to see him."

"Come with me," said the princess.

The lad followed the lovely princess to the throne room. In just a minute the king appeared, wearing his bright velvet clothes and his fine gold crown.

The lad fell on his knees before the king and said, "Oh, King, my father sent you these ripe, golden pears."

This time when the king uncovered the basket, what should he see but pears of real gold! The old witch had changed the ripe pears to gold.

"Now, my good lad," said the king, "here is a reward." He gave the boy fine velvet clothes and a box of gold coins.

Then he sent for the brothers who had been locked up and set them free. With great joy all three lads went home to their father.

A Bell for the Cat

Once upon a time some mice lived in a house that belonged to a poor, old man. No one bothered the mice. They scampered in and out of their holes dozens of times a day. They ran under tables and chairs, and they chased one another across the old wooden floors.

In and out of the kitchen cupboards they ran, looking for crumbs. No one bothered to lock the cupboard or even close the doors. So the mice nibbled happily when they found crumbs of bread or bits of cheese and pie.

It was a pleasant life for the mice. But one day a yellow cat came to live in the house. After that everything was different. The mice had an enemy.

If they crept out to look for crumbs in the cupboards, the cat appeared and chased them away.

"We can hardly snatch a crumb of dry bread or nibble at a bit of cheese," the mice complained.

It was true. The mice were not able to steal cheese or cake crumbs or even a tiny crumb of bread.

They knew they always would be hungry unless they got rid of the hated cat. She always would appear and chase them before they snatched a single crumb.

The mice kept complaining about their enemy. Finally they decided to get rid of her in some way.

They all got together and sat around in a half circle. But instead of planning, they just kept on complaining.

Finally a fat mouse stepped forward. He said, "During all this complaining I have done some thinking. I have thought of a clever plan. My plan won't get rid of the cat, but it will keep us safe."

"Oho, a plan!" squealed all the other mice. "Tell us about your plan."

Then the fat mouse told them about his fine plan.

"That wicked cat walks so softly we can't hear her," he said. "Let's fasten a bell around her neck. When she walks, the bell will ring. Then we'll know that she is near, and we can pop into our holes."

"That's a very clever plan!" cried one of the mice. "We'll fasten a bell around the cat's neck, and then we'll all be safe."

A wise old grandfather mouse had been leaning on his stick and thinking. Finally he stepped forward and spoke.

"That's a very clever plan," he said, "but somebody must fasten the bell on the cat. Let's decide who will do it."

"Not I! Not I! Not I!" cried several of the younger mice.

The grandfather mouse turned to the fat mouse who had thought of the plan. "Will you promise to fasten the bell on the cat yourself?" he asked.

"Oh, no!" answered the fat mouse.

No other mouse would promise to fasten the bell on the cat either.

"Then we must do as we always have done," said the grandfather mouse. "We must run when we can, or be caught when we can't. Remember! It is one thing to talk about a plan and another thing to make the plan work."

The Fisherman and His Wife

The Wonderful Fish

Long ago a fisherman and his wife lived near the sea. The man caught fish and sold them. That was the way he earned his living. But for weeks he had not sold any fish because he had not caught any.

Then one day he caught a beautiful golden fish.

"Here's a fine fish!" said the old man. "My wife can cook it for our supper."

But all at once the fish began to speak. "Please throw me back into the sea," it begged. "Please throw me back!"

"I've caught thousands of fish," the man said in great surprise. "But never before have I caught one that talked."

He felt so sorry for the fish that he decided to throw it back into the sea.

When the fish landed on the water, it stood up on its tail. "You shall have a reward for throwing me back," it said. "What would you like?"

The old man stood on the shore and tried to think of something he needed. But he could not think of a thing.

"Well," said the fish, "if you ever do need something, come to me. I promise that I will give you a good reward."

Then the fish dived into the sea.

When the fisherman returned to his hut, he told his wife about the fish.

"It wanted to give me a reward for throwing it back," he said. "But I could not think of a single thing I needed."

The Loaf of Bread

"I can't understand what you were thinking of," shouted his wife. "We haven't a crumb of bread or a piece of cheese. Our cupboard is empty. Yet you didn't ask for food. Go back and ask the fish for a loaf of bread."

The man knew that his wife would not stop complaining and scolding unless she had her own way. He went to the sea again. At the edge of the water, he called,

"Head in air and tail in sea.

Fish, fish, listen to me."

With a great splash of its tail, the golden fish appeared on the water.

"What do you want?" it asked.

"Our cupboard is empty," said the man. "We haven't even a bit of cheese or a loaf of bread. My wife sent me here to ask you for just a loaf of bread."

"Go home," said the fish as it flapped its tail and disappeared into the sea.

"Oh!" thought the old man. "What a scolding my wife will give me when I come home without a loaf of bread!"

But when he reached home, his wife was all smiles. A large loaf of bread had suddenly appeared in her cupboard.

The New House

The next day the fisherman's wife began to complain again. "A loaf of bread isn't much of a reward," she said. "Go and ask the fish for a new house. This hut is no better than a pigpen."

"I hardly dare to ask for so much," said her husband.

"Well!" said the old woman. "If the fish can give us a loaf of bread, it probably can give us a house also."

Once more the old man went to the sea. At the edge of the water he called the fish, and with a splash it appeared.

"My wife sent me here to ask for a new house," said the fisherman. "The roof and the walls of our hut are falling in. My wife says the hut is no better than a pigpen."

"Go home," said the fish as it flapped its tail and disappeared into the sea.

When the old man returned, he saw
a new house instead of the old hut.

"Welcome, husband!" cried his wife.
"See what the fish has given us."

She showed him three pretty rooms
with a new table and chairs and all the
things they needed.

In the cupboard were beautiful new
cups and plates and enough food to last
for a week.

The fisherman's wife was very happy
to have a new house instead of the hut.

A Queen in Her Palace

After two days the fisherman's wife began to complain again.

"This house is not big enough," she told her husband. "I have decided that I'll become a queen. I want to have a gold crown and wear fine velvet clothes instead of this ragged dress.

"Husband, go and tell the fish that I have decided to become a queen. I'll live in a palace with many servants."

"Oh, no, wife!" said the husband. "I would not dare to ask for such things."

But his wife sent him back to the sea. At the water's edge he called,

"Head in air and tail in sea.
Fish, fish, listen to me."

When the fish appeared, the man told it that his wife wanted to be a queen.

"Go home," said the fish as it flapped its tail and disappeared into the sea.

The fisherman returned home to find that his small hut had become a palace.

When he went inside, he saw his wife sitting like a queen on a gold throne. She wore a gold crown and was dressed in purple velvet trimmed with gold. Before her bowed two servants.

When she saw her poor husband in his ragged jacket, she screamed, "Away with you! Can't you see that a palace is too fine for a ragged old fisherman?

"Go and stay in the barn and make yourself useful there. A queen can't have a ragged fisherman in her palace."

The Storm

The ragged old man crept away. He hoped his wife would stop complaining since she had a throne and a palace.

But one day she sent for him and said, "I have decided to become queen of the waters. I'll have thousands and thousands of fish for my servants. Go to the sea and speak to the golden fish."

Against his wishes, the old man went down to the water's edge and called,

"Head in air and tail in sea.
Fish, fish, listen to me."

Suddenly a fierce storm made huge waves in the sea. The fish appeared on the sea and shouted, "What does your wife want now?"

"She wants to become queen of the waters and have thousands and thousands of fish for servants," said the old man.

The fish did not say a single word.

The wild storm grew worse and worse.
The wind whistled, the thunder roared,
and the rain poured down. The sea was
dark, and huge waves slapped against
the shore.

Then the fish dived to the bottom of
the sea, and the storm grew even wilder.

The old fisherman's knees knocked
together with fright. He shook with cold
in his ragged coat as the wind whistled
about him.

On the way home he decided not to tell
his wife what had happened. "I'll crawl
into the straw and hide," he thought.

But when he reached home, he rubbed his eyes in surprise. The huge palace was gone. The little old hut was back, and there were no servants around.

Inside he found his wife. She was wearing old ragged clothes instead of purple velvet and a crown, but she was singing merrily.

Now she was glad to see her husband, even if he was wearing a ragged jacket. They had bread and water for supper, and their plates and cups were cracked. But she never complained at all.

After that the old fisherman and his wife lived happily in their hut near the seashore. The wife never again spoke of a crown and a throne.

The husband caught many more fish. Sometimes one would shine in the sun. Then the old man would think of the golden fish, but it never appeared again.

The Princess Who Never Laughed

There was once a beautiful princess who had never laughed in her life.

The king loved his daughter, and he wanted her to laugh and be gay.

At last he sent servants throughout all the land. They told the people that any man who could make the princess laugh should have her for his wife.

Dozens of young men came to try their luck. They told jokes and did all sorts of tricks. The princess glanced at them now and then, but she never even smiled at their jokes and tricks.

Not far from the king's palace lived a poor lad named Peter.

The lad had often seen the beautiful princess sitting at her window, and now he heard of the king's promise.

"Maybe I can think of some trick to make the beautiful princess laugh," he said to himself.

He decided to try his luck, and off he went to the palace.

When he got there, he did not tell anyone that he had come to make the princess laugh.

Instead he pretended that he wanted work. He begged the cook to let him earn his living by helping her. The cook let him stay and put him to work carrying wood for the oven.

Every day as the lad worked, he kept watching for his chance to make the princess laugh.

One day when Peter went to the river to draw some water, he happened to catch a big fish in his pail.

On the way back he met an old woman leading a golden goose by a string.

"That's a fine bird you have," he said.

"No finer than that fish of yours," said the woman. "I'll trade my goose for your fish if you want to trade."

"Well," said Peter, "I might trade."

"If you knew what a wonderful goose it is, you would trade," said the woman. "Everyone who sees the goose stops to pet it. Then if you say some magic words, the people stick fast."

"That goose might be useful to me," said Peter. "Maybe I will trade my fish for it. Tell me the magic words."

The woman said, "The magic words are, 'If you care to come along, hang on.'"

So Peter traded his fish for the goose.

Before long Peter met a servant girl wearing a yellow cap and apron.

"Let me pet your goose," she said.

"You had better not," said Peter, and he pretended to hurry. "You might pull out some of its golden feathers."

But the servant girl began to pet the goose.

Quick as a wink Peter said, "If you care to come along, hang on."

How the girl did fight to get loose! She kicked and screamed, but of course she could not pull herself free. She had to hang on and go with Peter.

Soon they met the girl's father. He saw his daughter kicking and fighting to pull herself loose. So he took hold of her arms and began to pull, too.

"If you care to come along, hang on," shouted Peter.

Of course the man stuck fast to his daughter, who was stuck fast to the golden goose. They kicked, and they screamed, but they could not pull loose.

"They have to hang on," thought Peter. "This is a very useful bird. I'm glad I traded my fish for this treasure."

The next one to get stuck was a man playing a fiddle. When Peter said the magic words, the man had to hang on, too. Next a gardener carrying a hoe and a rake got stuck.

Then Peter led his queer parade past the window where the princess sat.

She pretended not to notice, but twice Peter saw her glance out and smile.

"Oho!" he thought. "Probably she will laugh soon. This goose of mine is a real treasure."

Soon he stopped his parade below the window where the princess sat.

During all this time the man kept on playing his fiddle. People were coming out of the palace to dance in a big circle. As they danced, they sang,

"Heel and toe, heel and toe.
Dancing, dancing, round we go."

The cook left her oven and rushed out to join the others. She was in such a hurry that she still carried a big pan and had a spot of flour on her nose. She began dancing in the circle also.

"Ho, ho!" cried the gardener, waving his hoe and rake. "Look at the cook prancing around in her white apron. Doesn't she look silly with that spot of flour on her nose?"

"Silly, am I?" said the cook, giving the gardener a slap on the back.

This was the very chance that Peter wanted. He called, "If you care to come along, hang on."

Just then the cook stuck fast to the gardener's jacket. She scolded, kicked, and pulled in her fight to get free. But she had to hang on and go where Peter went.

Peter glanced at the princess to see if she was watching the funny sight. She was leaning forward, and Peter noticed a real smile on her face.

"Oho!" he thought. "Now she's going to laugh. She can't help herself."

Then for the first time in her life, the princess did laugh! She opened her mouth wide and laughed so hard that tears ran down her face. The king had to hold his daughter to keep her from falling.

The king laughed, and Peter laughed. And so did the people who were stuck together. They laughed so hard that they shook all over. And they shook so hard that they all came loose.

Of course the king kept his promise. He gave Peter the princess for his wife and gave him a crown and a golden throne besides.

And Peter and the beautiful princess lived happily ever after.

Mother Hulda

The Beautiful Daughter

Once upon a time there was a woman who had two daughters. One of them was beautiful, but the other one was ugly. The beautiful daughter worked hard, but the other daughter did nothing at all.

The beautiful maiden milked the cows, scrubbed the floors, made the butter, and baked the bread.

But the ugly girl would not bake or scrub or do any hard work at all. The floors could stay dirty, and the cupboard could be empty, and still she would not work.

One day the beautiful maiden went to the well for a pail of water. She got down on her knees at the edge of the well and leaned over to draw up the pail.

The maiden leaned over so far that she fell head first into the well.

Down, down, down she went.

The next thing she knew, she was in a beautiful meadow full of red roses and white Easter lilies.

There was a path among the flowers. As the girl walked along the path, she wondered where it would lead her.

Soon she came to a queer little house with a high, pointed roof. Just then an old woman popped her head out of the window. When the maiden glanced up and saw an ugly old woman, she started to run away in fright.

But the ugly woman called to her in a pleasant voice, "Don't be afraid, my dear child. I am Mother Hulda. Come into my house and talk to me."

Mother Hulda looked as ugly as an old troll, but her voice was so kind that the maiden was not frightened any more. She walked into the house.

Then Mother Hulda invited the maiden to live with her. "You may work for me," she said. "If you are a good helper, I will treat you very kindly. I will treat you as if you were my own daughter."

So the maiden decided to stay with Mother Hulda.

Mother Hulda said, "You must make
my bed carefully every day. You must
learn to shake the pillows until all the
feathers scatter in the air. When you
do this, snow falls on the earth."

So the maiden pounded and shook the
pillows until the feathers flew around.

"That is right," said Mother Hulda.
"Shake the pillows. Make the feathers
fly. Then snow will fall on the earth."

The maiden stayed and worked hard.
Mother Hulda liked the way she shook
the pillows. So she treated her kindly.
She treated her like a daughter.

One day the maiden said to Mother Hulda, "You have treated me well during my stay here. You have treated me like a daughter, but I miss my mother and sister. Please, may I go back to them?"

"Yes, dear child," said Mother Hulda. "You may go now." And she led the girl to a door that opened before them.

As the maiden went through the door, a rain of gold coins poured down. The coins stuck to her clothes, so that she was covered with gold from head to toe.

"That is the reward you have earned by helping me," said Mother Hulda.

Then the maiden found herself at the edge of her mother's yard.

A rooster was on the fence. When he saw the maiden all covered with gold coins, he flapped his wings and crowed,

"Er-er-roo! Er-er-er-roo!

Your golden girl is back with you."

The maiden said to her mother and sister, "I have been at Mother Hulda's. She treated me kindly during my stay. She treated me like a daughter. All these gold coins are a reward for helping her. You may have them, Mother, and we'll all live here together."

The Ugly Daughter

When the lazy girl heard her sister's story, she thought she probably could get some gold, too. She ran straight to the edge of the well and jumped in.

Everything happened just as it had happened to her sister. When the lazy girl opened her eyes, she was in the beautiful meadow among the roses and Easter lilies.

She hurried down the path because she could hardly wait to get to Mother Hulda's house.

The girl did not feel any fright at all when the ugly old woman leaned out of the window.

Then Mother Hulda invited the lazy girl to stay and work for her.

The girl promised that she would help Mother Hulda. But her thoughts were on the gold coins she would be paid.

Mother Hulda showed the ugly girl how to shake the feather pillows and make snow fall on the earth.

The first day the maiden shook the pillows until the feathers were scattered about, and snow fell on the earth.

The second day she decided that she would not work very hard. She just pretended to shake the pillows.

By the fifth day the lazy girl did not even pretend to work.

Mother Hulda called her, but the girl answered crossly, "I am not going to work. It is foolish to shake those pillows every day, and the house isn't very dirty. I'm not going to work."

Finally Mother Hulda came to the girl's room and said, "Get up, my girl. You are going home today."

This was what the girl wanted to hear. "Now," she thought, "I'll get the gold."

But when Mother Hulda led the girl to the door, sticky black tar poured over her from head to toe.

"This is your reward for the way you helped me," said Mother Hulda.

The next minute the girl found herself at the edge of her mother's yard.

When the rooster saw the girl with sticky tar all over her, he crowed,

"Er-er-roo! Er-er-er-roo!

Your tar-black girl is back with you!"

The tar did not come off the girl until she stopped being lazy. And it was a long time before she learned that lesson.

The new *Streets and Roads* has a total vocabulary of 1280 words. Of these, 401 words are new at this level; 315 were introduced at Book Two² level; 229 were new at Book Two¹ level; 177 were introduced at Book One level; 100 were new in the Primer; and the remaining 58 were introduced at Pre-Primer level.

Each of the 401 words is used a minimum of eight times in the new *Streets and Roads*. The first three uses of the 401 words are bunched for easy mastery; there is no gap of more than five pages between any two of these first three uses. Thereafter, at spaced intervals, there are at least five more uses of each word.

The 401 new words used in the new *Streets and Roads* are listed below. The following inflected or derived forms of known words are not counted as new words: possessives; plural nouns in *s, es;* verb forms in *s, es, d, ed, ing;* forms made by adding *er* of agent, *er* or *est* of comparison, *en, ly,* and *y;* forms regular except for the change of *y* to *i,* the dropping of *e,* or the doubling of a consonant before an ending. Compounds of known words and parts of previously learned hyphenated compounds are not counted, nor are contractions in which the apostrophe represents only one omitted letter. Letters representing sounds that are not words are not counted. Also, homographs are not counted as separate words; for example, if *leaves* as the plural of *leaf* has been introduced, *leaves* as the third person of the verb *leave* is not counted as a separate word.

*The red asterisks indicate 283 words that children should be able to attack independently by applying the word-attack skills learned at this and preceding levels in The New Basic Reading Program. The methods of attack children can use in unlocking each of these 283 words are given in the lesson plans in the *Guidebook* for the new *Streets and Roads*.

WORD LIST

Unit I			
	9 held *	15 I'd	21 picnic
	breath	16	rode *
5	10 close	17 felt *	22 different
6 Hall *	11	air	sail *
7 flapping *	12 we'll	18	23 grove *
safe *	13	19	drove *
8 mind *	14 halfway	20 glass *	24 passing *
	ladder	cage *	automobile

25 ahead
26 .....
27 .....
28 .....
29 seat *
30 wheel *
    nobody
31 pound *
    crowd *
32 stuck *
33 awful
34 .....
35 fancy *
    invited
36 wearing
    suit
37 wore *
    purple
38 uncover
39 silver
40 wrong *
41 sandwiches
    pieces
42 dozens
43 elevator
    fifth *
44 hour
45 bicycles
    hundreds
46 .....
47 puzzled
    either
48 .....
49 .....
50 trade *
    Friday
51 .....
52 monkey
53 bunch *
    buttons
54 anybody
55 true *
56 Don *

UNIT II

57 .....
58 tickets
    bus *
59 .....
60 rows *
    raise *
61 mine *
62 suppose
63 plan *
64 .....
65 .....
66 they'll *
67 jam *
    Sarah
68 desks *
    draw *
    wasps
69 .....
70 rid *
    sweet *
71 hate *
    sight *
72 carefully
73 .....
74 .....
75 fierce
    giraffe
    spoke *
76 Judy
77 .....
78 tents *
    loaded *
79 certainly
80 acts *
81 drew *
    finally
82 band *
    ring *
    bowed *
83 clapped *

84 buggy
85 .....
86 eight
    course
87 ought *
88 decide
    threw *
89 .....
90 .....
91 whoa *
92 .....
93 Benny's *
    marching *
    toot *
94 fair *
    sold *
95 mistake
    able
96 begin
    Tuesday
97 win *
    prize *
98 tight *
    fastened
99 sizes *
    hitched *
100 rang *
101 belonged
102 ribbon *
103 shadow
104 nine *
    racing
105 .....
106 airplane *
    between
    pasture *
107 finish
    mile *
    eleven
108 nails *
    already
109 circle
    landed *

110 twenty *
    north *
111 luck *
112 below
    lower *
113 .....
114 traveling
    trimmed *
115 child
    secret
116 walls *
    holly *
117 Santa *
    Claus *
118 gift *
    chocolate
    fruit *
119 led *
    underneath
120 porch *
121 song *
    jingle
122 .....

UNIT III

123 .....
124 Beaver *
    jacket *
125 farther *
126 grumble *
127 shakes *
128 behave *
129 .....
130 polite *
    welcome *
131 Tippy *
    naughty
    frisky *
132 smash *
    pail *
133 trunk *
    snatched *
    peanuts *

318

ILLUSTRATIONS

The pictures in this book were made by William Neebe, Fredman-Chaite Studios, Inc., Nell Stolp Smock, Herbert Rudeen, Walter Alois Weber, Keith Ward, Earl Sherwan, Donn P. Crane, Connie Moran, and Jack White.

ACKNOWLEDGMENTS

For permission to adapt and use copyrighted material, grateful acknowledgment is made to the author and publisher for "The Queer Noise" from "The Haunted Skyscraper" by J. Flory, copyright 1946 by Story Parade, Inc., reprinted by permission; to the author for "Baby-Sitting with Tommy" from "Time Is Funny" by E. R. Montgomery; for "The Picnic Place" from "The Hollyberrys and the Hot Day" by A. Dalgliesh; to authors and publishers for "The Big, Long Honk" from "A Great Big Honk" by A. J. Stalson in *Junior Home for Mothers;* for "A Halloween Surprise" from "The Little Pumpkin Guests" by R. G. Plowhead, "Lost and Found" by C. R. Brink, "Tippy Elephant's Hat" by J. Norris, "Paddy's Christmas" by H. A. Monsell, "Button-Eyes and the Prize" from "Surprise Performance" by L. R. Davis, "Miss Molly Squeak" from "Miss Tilly Skreek" by Bertha Y. Burrill, all in *Child Life;* for "Let's Trade" from "The Swapping Party" by R. L. Holberg, "Salt for the Deer" from "Deer Tamer" by R. J. Canfield, both in *Jack and Jill;* to the author for "Who Wants This Dog?" from "Slippy and the Neighbor's Chickens" by E. H. Doolittle; to authors and publishers for "Bread and Jam" from *Ju-Ju and His Friends* by M. Van Vrooman: Albert Whitman & Co.; for "Big Joe and Little Joe" from "Big 'Bo and Little 'Bo" by R. Stone from *Trails for Juniors,* copyright 1950, used by permission; for "Finding a Friend" from "Janie's Wish" by M. Lawrence, copyright 1947 by Story Parade, Inc., reprinted by permission; for "Benny's Trick" from "Fuzzy Wuzz" by M. P. Meigs, "The Story of White Satin" by B. J. Dearborn, both in *Junior Home;* for "How Tom Went to the Fair" from "The Silver Lining" by E. P. Milbanke in *The Youth's Companion;* for "The Traveling Christmas Party" from *Calico* by E. C. Phillips: Houghton Mifflin Company; for "A Ride to Animal Town" by M. C. Potter in *American Childhood;* for "Sojo" by E. Berry: The Harter Publishing Company; for "Fluffytail and the Peanut Hunt" from "Fluffytail's Peanut Hunt" by M. H. Comfort in *Boys and Girls:* Whitmore and Smith; for "Chip, the Baby Chipmunk" from "Chipper, the Bold" by E. Hammond in *Wee Wisdom;* for "The Bears' Picnic" from "When Three Yellowstone Bears Attended a Picnic" in *Uncle Sam's Animals* by F. M. Fox, copyright 1927 by the Century Co.; for "Ringtail, the Young Raccoon" from *Ringtail* by A. C. Gall and F. H. Crew: Oxford University Press; for "Paddle Tail" from *The Beaver Twins* by J. Tompkins, copyright 1940 by Frederick A. Stokes Co.; for "Chuckle Makes a Friend" from *Chuckle: The Story of a Woodchuck* by David M. Stearns, copyright 1939 and reprinted by permission of Rinehart & Company, Inc., Publishers; for "The Lad and the North Wind" from "The Lad Who Went to the North Wind" by G. W. Dasent: G. P. Putnam's Sons; and for "The Golden Pears" in *Stories and Story-Telling* by A. M. Keyes: D. Appleton and Company.

Acknowledgment is also made to the Harris Estate for "Brother Rabbit and Tar Baby" from "The Wonderful Tar-Baby Story" by J. C. Harris; and to W. S. Sloan for "Lady and the Black Dog" from "Shadows" by E. V. Sloan.